STUDENTS'/TRAINEES' [

BUSINESS
administration

Level II

Carolyn Andrew
Elm Park College, Stanmore

Marian Clough
City & Guilds Verifier

Jean Davenport
formerly Tile Hill College, Coventry

Margaret Harradine
Elm Park College, Stanmore

Eileen Jackson
Hertford Regional College

Anna Kennedy
Tile Hill College, Coventry

Susan Smith
Greenhill College, Harrow

JOHN MURRAY
in association with

City and Guilds

Business Administration NVQ Level I Students'/Trainees' Book
ISBN 0–7195–4845–4
Tutor's Resource Pack ISBN 0–7195–4847–0
Business Administration NVQ Level II Students'/Trainees' Book
ISBN 0–7195–4846–2
Tutor's Resource Pack ISBN 0–7195–4944–2

ACKNOWLEDGEMENTS

The authors and publishers are grateful to the following for permitting reproduction of copyright material:
J. Parker Dutch Bulbs (Wholesale) Ltd for bulbs advertisement from the *Daily Telegraph Magazine Autumn 1990 Choice* p. 38

Diagram p. 53 by John Townson/Creation

© Carolyn Andrew, Marian Clough, Jean Davenport, Margaret Harradine, Eileen Jackson, Anna Kennedy, Susan Smith 1991

First published 1991 by
John Murray (Publishers) Ltd
50 Albemarle Street
London W1X 4BD

in association with
City & Guilds of London Institute
46 Britannia Street
London WC1X 9RG

British Library Cataloguing in Publication Data
Business administration — level II:
Students'/trainees' book.
  I. Andrew, Carolyn
  651.3068

  ISBN 0–7195–4846–2

Filmset by Wearside Tradespools, Boldon, Tyne and Wear
Printed in Great Britain by Thomson Litho Ltd, East Kilbride

FOREWORD

City and Guilds of London Institute has a long history of providing assessments and certification to those who have undertaken education and training in a wide variety of technical subjects or occupational areas. Its business is essentially to provide an assurance that pre-determined standards have been met. That activity has grown in importance over the past few years as government and national bodies strive to create the right conditions for the steady growth of a skilled and flexible workforce.

Both teachers and learners need materials to support them as they work towards the attainment of qualifications, and City and Guilds is pleased to be working with a number of distinguished publishers towards meeting that need. It has been closely involved in planning, author selection and text appraisal, but the opinions expressed in the publications are those of the authors and not necessarily those of the Institute.

City and Guilds is fully committed to the projects listed below and is pleased to commend them to teaching staff, students and their advisers.

Carolyn Andrew *et al.*, *Business Administration Level I* and *Business Administration Level II*, John Murray
David Minton, *Teaching Skills in Further & Adult Education*, Macmillan
Graham Morris & Leslie Reveler, *Retail Certificate Workbook* (Levels I and II), Macmillan
Peter Riley (Consultant Editor), *Computer-aided Engineering*, Macmillan
Tim Roberts, *Wine Appreciation*, Stanley Thornes
Barbara Wilson, *Information Technology: The Basics*, Macmillan
Caroline Wilkinson, *Information Technology in the Office*, Macmillan

BUSINESS ADMINISTRATION

City and Guilds Business Administration scheme (4400) was designed to accord with the standards of competence laid down by the Administrative Business and Commercial Training Group. Accredited as a National Vocational Qualification, Business Administration is assessed by means of ensuring that candidates are able to reach competence in the wide range of office skills in a workplace situation.

The aim of these *Business Administration* publications is to assist in the process of reaching that competence. The tasks have been designed to meet the standards of the scheme. In certain circumstances it may be possible to use the correctly completed assignments as part of the evidence that the student has reached the necessary standard, although obviously simulation cannot truly substitute for practice and assessment in the workplace.

CONTENTS

UNIT 10

CREATING AND MAINTAINING BUSINESS RELATIONSHIPS

ELEMENT 10.1 *Create and maintain professional relationships with other members of staff*

INTRODUCTION

What do you have to do?

▷ deal with requests from colleagues promptly and willingly

▷ pass on essential information to colleagues promptly and accurately

▷ ask politely for help when you need it

▷ when sharing work with colleagues, agree on areas of responsibility and workload

▷ if you have problems or difficulties in any working relationships, try to sort them out by discussion, or report the situation accurately to your supervisor

How well do you have to do it?

To achieve this you must be able to:

▷ establish good relationships with your colleagues

▷ play your part in creating a cheerful, pleasant working atmosphere

What do you need to know?

▷ your job description

▷ what else you could reasonably and safely be asked to do

▷ what is expected of you in terms of behaviour and appearance

▷ how to contact people within your organisation using internal communication systems – for example, telephones, electronic mailboxes, pagers and loudspeakers

▷ your own and your employer's responsibilities under the Health and Safety at Work Act

▷ how to organise and complete your work within a given deadline

BACKGROUND KNOWLEDGE

Every employee needs to know his/her job description and where s/he fits into the organisation.

- Have you seen a copy of your job description?
- Have you seen an organisation chart for your workplace/training centre?
- Are you familiar with the safety policy of your organisation and are you aware of your obligations under the Health and Safety at Work Act?

You may often be asked to do more work than you can complete in the time given. You will therefore need to **prioritise**. Ask yourself the following:

- What *must* be done urgently?
- Would failure to do one of the jobs mean someone else could not complete his/her work?
- What could you leave till later?
- Is anyone free to help you?

You may be asked to undertake tasks outside your job description. Try to weigh up whether it is a reasonable request. You need to consider the following:

- Your current workload – do you have time to help?
- Would a refusal cause difficulties for a colleague?
- Is it a task you are competent to tackle?

At work you are expected to behave in a professional manner – this means being thoughtful and considerate when dealing with your colleagues. Your communication with others, whether verbal, written or even your body language, must always reflect this professional attitude.

If you do encounter serious difficulties in your working relationships it is important to face them and discuss them openly. If you cannot sort them out, then refer to your supervisor.

THE CASE STUDIES

In this unit it is more appropriate to refer to case studies rather than tasks.

How would you deal with the following?

CASE STUDY 1

You are employed as an administrative assistant and you see a member of the Reprographics Department stacking a new delivery of paper against a fire door. You realise the implications of this should there be an emergency and you tactfully point this out. He tells you 'where to go'.

What will you do now?

CASE STUDY 2

A senior colleague is in an important meeting. It is 5.30 p.m. and you receive a telephone message from her husband saying that there is a power cut, the baby's crying, there's no supper and can she bring home a takeaway as quickly as possible.

Write out the message and state how you would get it to her.

CASE STUDY 3

Your organisation has to produce a mail shot at short notice. Although this is not normally part of your job, you have been asked by the Marketing Manager's secretary to help and you offer to insert the mail shots in envelopes, seal them and affix the address labels. You have been working at this for about an hour when you see the secretary sipping tea and hear her chatting on the phone. You still have a huge pile of envelopes to deal with – you feel you have been used!

What are you going to say to her?

CASE STUDY 4

At the suggestion of your manager you have attended a two-day supervisor's training course to prepare you for possible promotion. On your return you find your work-station piled high with outstanding work although you had arranged with two colleagues that they would deal with any urgent matters in your absence, and your manager had agreed to this arrangement.

You now find two urgent pieces of work that have not been done. There is a curt note from your manager asking for the finished work. You explain that these tasks are going to take most of the morning and he gets very angry as he needs them for a meeting at 10.00 a.m.

What will you say to your manager, and how will you raise this matter with your colleagues?

For competence to be credited you will need to be observed over a period of time in your workplace/training centre.

ELEMENT 10.2 *Create and maintain professional relationships with customers and clients*

INTRODUCTION

What do you have to do?

▷ greet all customers and clients promptly and politely

▷ welcome known customers by name in an appropriate and friendly manner

▷ when talking with customers and clients, promote good will and trust

▷ take into account pressures of work when talking to customers and clients

▷ refer customers and clients promptly to a more senior colleague if you cannot help them

▷ always follow any specific policies concerning dealings with customers and clients that your organisation may have

▷ explain any delays politely

What do you need to know?

▷ greeting styles used by your organisation

▷ how to deal with difficult customers and clients

▷ your organisation's legal obligations to the public

▷ any policies you must follow concerning confidential information

▷ how your organisation wishes to handle complaints

▷ how you can do all this and keep your customers and clients well-informed and happy

▷ how to recognise non-verbal communication signals, such as signs of anxiety, embarrassment, nerves, impatience, etc.

BACKGROUND KNOWLEDGE

Every employee needs to know the policies of his/her organisation concerning dealings with customers and clients.

● Does your organisation have such a policy, and if so, have you seen it?

● Are you familiar with the legal obligations of your organisation to the public such as Public Liability, and the Trade Descriptions Act?

Ask yourself the following:

● Do you always behave in a professional way?

● Do you present a good image of your organisation?

● Do you think people enjoy meeting you? If not, why not?

● Do you take the trouble to look for, and respond to, body language in others?

You have already looked at working with your colleagues in Element 10.1. The same good practice should be followed in all business relationships. If you do find yourself unable to cope with a difficult client or customer, don't be afraid to refer to a senior colleague and learn from his/her handling of the situation.

THE CASE STUDIES

How would you deal with the following situations?

CASE STUDY 1

You are employed in the Enquiries Office at your local College of Further Education. You have a large sign displayed: 'Sorry, no change given'. The college policy is that change must not be given as students constantly disturbed the office staff for this purpose. It is mid-afternoon and you are busy with your work. A young student rushes to the office in some distress, saying that she must use the telephone urgently but has no change.
    What would you do?

CASE STUDY 2

It is lunchtime. You are alone in the Sales Department when the telephone rings. It is an angry caller who wants to know immediately where his order is – your organisation had apparently promised delivery before 10.00 a.m. this morning. He is threatening to cancel his order.
    What would you say to calm him down?

CASE STUDY 3

You are working in the Personnel Department of a large organisation and you have just typed a reference for a current member of staff who has applied for promotion with another company. You receive a telephone call from the prospective employer explaining that the interview is taking place now and the reference has not yet been received. They apparently have two good candidates for the job and wish to make an offer to one of them today. They cannot appoint without references.
    They ask whether your boss can give them a verbal reference immediately. Your boss is unavailable, and it is your organisation's policy not to give confidential information over the telephone.
    What would you do?

UNIT 11

PROVIDING INFORMATION TO CUSTOMERS/CLIENTS

ELEMENT 11.1 *Respond to customers'/clients' specific requests for information on products/services offered by the organisation*

ELEMENT 11.2 *Inform customers/clients about available products and services*

These two elements have been combined as they link together and in business would not be separated.

INTRODUCTION

What do you have to do?

▷ respond to customer/client requests promptly and politely

▷ make sure that requests for privacy are respected

▷ maintain confidentiality at all times

▷ know when to refer situations to your supervisor

▷ make sure that you suggest products which match the customer's/client's requirements

▷ make sure you give the information as promptly as possible

▷ where information is not immediately available, explain this to the customer/client and make arrangements to call him/her back, or to find out

▷ make accurate calculations when giving examples of prices, discounts, etc.

▷ make certain that your records of interviews are always accurate and up to date

▷ ensure that any action that has been agreed is followed up

▷ note and reorder written materials to avoid running out of them

How well do you have to do it?

To achieve this you must be able to:

▷ handle correctly all contacts with customers/clients

▷ represent your organisation and be professional at all times – if you are not, you may find that your organisation will hold you responsible for losing business

What do you need to know?

Any of the following may be face-to-face or on the telephone:

▷ how to greet your organisation's customers/clients

▷ all about your organisation's products and services

▷ how to recognise non-verbal communication signals, such as signs of anxiety, anger, etc.

▷ how to respond to such signals

▷ how to deal with difficult/aggressive/distressed customers/clients

▷ how to find out efficiently what the customer/client wants to know

▷ how to access paper-based and computerised information sources

▷ how to reorder written materials as required

▷ where to find any written information you may need to give to clients

▷ what information you are permitted to give, and when you need to refer to a supervisor

▷ how to write a brief record of your interview with the customer/client

▷ how the Public Liability Act, the Financial Services Act and the Trade Descriptions Act affect your work

BACKGROUND KNOWLEDGE

In any job you may be expected to deal with members of the public. This is particularly important if your job involves dealing with customers or clients who may be going to spend a considerable amount of money with your firm.

You will need to make sure that you understand your organisation's policy on the following issues:

● when a client needs to be seen in private – for example, in a firm of solicitors. A client may be distressed and embarrassed to talk in front of other people.

● when information must be treated with complete confidentiality – for example, discounts offered to specific customers, or any customers on whom you may have made a credit check.

You will be required to keep accurate records of all your discussions with customers/clients in case you or anyone else needs to refer to the content at a later date. For instance, prices given to a customer over the telephone will need to be confirmed in writing.

You will naturally need to know all about your organisation's products. You should make sure that you have all the up-to-date information, such as catalogues and price lists.

You will need to know about paper-based and computerised sources of information. This will include files, catalogues, stock records and databases. You should be aware of the different ways of reordering supplies of written material, such as catalogues, forms, price lists, etc. You should be able to assess when you will need to reorder, and how to do it.

Sometimes you may be asked for information concerning confidential matters, such as prices quoted to other customers or personal information about clients. You must be very careful not to give this information to the wrong people. If in doubt, check with your supervisor.

You will always need to use the utmost tact and discretion when dealing with customers and clients. You should be sincere, keen to help and businesslike, and remember that you are representing your organisation. If you are unable to give an immediate answer to a query and you have promised to find out and call the customer back, do so as soon as possible!

Even on the most difficult day, with the most difficult customer, you will have to stay calm.

THE CASE STUDIES

Scenario 1

You are working in the Sales Department of Leisurewear Limited. In Unit 15 *Reception*, you will find Background Knowledge on Leisurewear Ltd and an organisation chart for the company. You will need to refer to these.

It is Tuesday afternoon and you are very busy updating the computerised price lists. How would you deal with the following situations?

CASE STUDY 1

There is an incoming telephone call. The customer requires the price of tracksuits, model number HG768. You have not yet entered this on the computer and you only have the old price to hand. The price increase is 7.25 per cent and the old price was £22.50 for orders of less than 12, and £20.00 for orders over 12.

CASE STUDY 2

A buyer from a large retailer has arrived to look at the new season's range and to discuss special discounts. It is your job to meet her and show her the range in the showroom, and to discuss quantities and standard trade discounts. The Sales Manager is the only person who is permitted to negotiate special prices. Tina Allen, the Sales Manager, was due to meet the buyer, but is off sick. You realise that you should have contacted the buyer to change the appointment, but you forgot.

CASE STUDY 3

The telephone rings. An angry customer is complaining that a recent delivery of football strip has arrived, and instead of being black on red it is navy on red. You check the order, and discover that the customer's order states 'black', but the handwritten note of his original telephone order states 'navy'. It would appear that whoever took the message got it wrong, and passed it to Production before the written confirmation order was received.

CASE STUDY 4

The telephone rings. A local playgroup wishes to order playsuits for 3–5 year olds. The parents are to be asked to pay for the suits, and so the cost must be kept low. However, the suits will have to be hardwearing, and suitable for vigorous play. You check the catalogue entry, which is as follows:

Ref. no.	Description	Price	Discounts
FG464	Nylon suit	£3.99	10% on orders of 12+
FG465	Cotton/nylon suit	£5.99	10% on orders of 12+
FG466	100% cotton suit	£7.99	10% on orders of 12+
FG467	Polycotton suit	£6.99	10% on orders of 12+
FG468	Woollen suit	£8.99	10% on orders of 12+

You know from previous experience that the most hardwearing suit is FG466, but that FG467 is a popular choice with retailers, as it is 'easy-care'.

CASE STUDY 5

The telephone rings. It is a regular customer enquiring about a delivery date for an order placed two weeks ago. You check the file and find that it has been held up because the customer has not settled his account.

CASE STUDY 6

Reception rings you. There is a potential new customer who wishes to have information regarding credit payment terms for large orders. It is company policy never to discuss this until the credit rating of a customer has been checked. You check your files and find that you have no information regarding this company.

CASE STUDY 7

You have completely run out of telephone order message sheets. You never liked them anyway and have always meant to redesign them. Now is your chance. Design a message sheet which is suitable for accurately recording incoming telephone enquiries to the Sales Office.

CASE STUDY 8

The local Chamber of Commerce has written to Leisurewear informing them that they intend to produce a directory of environmentally friendly companies. Draft a box advertisement to be included in the directory stressing the following points:

Name:
Leisurewear Limited
Lion House
LICHESTER LI2 7PR

Telephone number: 0427 456784
Fax number: 0427 419885

Leisurewear use recycled paper in their offices.
They use environmentally friendly manufacturing methods.
All company cars use unleaded petrol.

CASE STUDY 9

Compose a short letter to the Chamber of Commerce at Commerce House, Lichester LI3 4LB, enclosing the advertisement for inclusion in their directory and at the same time inviting any interested members to contact Leisurewear Limited with a view to visiting the factory to test how 'green' Leisurewear is.

CASE STUDY 10

A customer writes asking for the latest catalogue. Write a short reply explaining that the new catalogues are still at the printers and you will forward one as soon as possible. You don't want to lose a customer, so be careful how you write your letter.

Scenario 2

You are working for Lichester Insurance Services, insurance brokers who offer a wide range of insurance and assurance services. It is a small company with a good local reputation. Other members of staff are:

John Goodbody – General Manager
Jayne Wilkinson – Motor Insurance specialist
Reena Patel – Life Assurance specialist
Patrick O'Grady – Household Insurance specialist
Darren White – Clerical Assistant
Sara Henson – Receptionist
You – Trainee Insurance Clerk

CASE STUDY 1

You are the first to arrive, at 8.30 a.m. each morning, and your first job is to listen to the telephone answering machine messages. What action would you take in response to the following?

(a) Hello – this is Mr Smith of 28 The Grove, Lichester, and we've been burgled. I've informed the police and they said I should contact you straightaway. I can't find the insurance policy. Can you please help me?

(b) My name is Peter Prentice and my car insurance ran out last month. I didn't realise this until I checked my policy last night, because I've been involved in an accident. Am I covered?

(c) Hello, Jayne, it's Roger here – sorry to have to leave a message like this, but I've had to go away urgently and can't keep to our arrangements. We still need that quote on fleet insurance rates ASAP. By the way, can you send me your best quote for life assurance for me? I know this isn't your area, but can you pass it on? Thanks.

CASE STUDY 2

You act for a couple who have recently separated. The wife calls in asking for details of her husband's endowment policy, which is due to mature this year. She is very insistent, and breaks down in tears. How would you deal with her?

CASE STUDY 3

A smart-looking man walks into the office stating that he is a local magistrate seeking a motor insurance quote. He has heard that your company offers preferential rates to certain professions. What details would you record so that Jayne Wilkinson can deal with this on her return from lunch?

CASE STUDY 4

You are on the Reception desk during the lunch hour and a regular client arrives to find out the premium if he adds his 17-year-old son to his motor insurance policy. You call up the computer database to find this information and the program crashes. You cannot now give this information to the client immediately, so what alternative arrangements would you suggest?

CASE STUDY 5

You receive a letter from a prospective client asking about insurance for his caravan. He wants to know whether it can be covered on his normal household policy. Patrick asks you to compose a letter explaining that Lichester Insurance Services need more information, as caravans must be quoted separately from household insurance. You need to know the value of the caravan and the security arrangements, plus other details. Ask the prospective client either to call in tomorrow or to telephone Patrick.

CASE STUDY 6

A client who has his household contents insured through Lichester Insurance Services telephones to say that his son, at college in Cambridge, has had his bicycle stolen. He wants to know whether this is covered on his normal policy. You check the policy and find that he is definitely not covered. Draft a polite letter explaining this to the client.

CASE STUDY 7

You have been asked to prepare a quote for motor insurance. The basic premium is £450. The client is entitled to a discount of 5 per cent because he is a teacher, another 2.5 per cent because he lives out of town, and a further 50 per cent No Claims discount. Work out the amount he has to pay and compose a letter advising him of this. His name is Frederick Chalmers, and his address is 45 Bush Road, Nether Region Village LI10 7TH.

CASE STUDY 8

In order to ensure that your clients know exactly what your company offers, you place a regular advertisement in the local paper. You have been asked to draft a new version for next month. The old version looked like this:

LICHESTER INSURANCE SERVICES

can help with all your insurance needs.

Be assured of a friendly welcome from our team of specialists:

Robert Burns – General Manager
Jayne Wilkinson – Motor queries
Reena Patel – Life Assurance specialist

The old newspaper advertisement

You will see that this is quite out of date. Amend the incorrect information and add the *specialist* personnel who now work for Lichester Insurance Services. Add a line or two at the bottom telling potential clients that your company is offering a mortgage service as from next month.

STORING AND SUPPLYING INFORMATION

ELEMENT 12.1 *Maintain an established filing system*

INTRODUCTION

What do you have to do?

▷ maintain and control an established filing system

How well do you have to do it?

To achieve this you must be able to:

▷ demonstrate competence in relation to the performance criteria in Unit 1 *Filing*:

Element 1.1 *File documents and open new files within an established filing system*

Element 1.2 *Identify and retrieve documents from within an established filing system*

▷ record and control all file and document movements accurately

▷ identify overdue files and documents and implement systems for their prompt return

▷ ensure that all files are maintained in good condition in the correct location

▷ identify out-of-date documents, extract them from the system and follow laid-down procedures for dealing with them

▷ identify new files and label them legibly for insertion into the existing system

▷ ensure the confidentiality and security of information is always maintained

▷ maintain safety procedures at all times

What do you need to know?

▷ how to classify, sort, handle and store documents

▷ how to complete simple forms/records to control the movement of documents

▷ how to file documents using indexing and cross-referencing systems (such as alphabetical, numerical, geographical, subject, chronological)

▷ how to identify and use different filing methods and equipment (such as lateral, vertical, computer-based)

▷ how to operate safely office equipment used in connection with filing (such as staplers and shredders)

▷ how to identify and use circulation lists

▷ how to identify and state relevant aspects of the Data Protection Act

What do you need to be able to do?

▷ record file movements

▷ maintain files in good condition

▷ introduce new files into the system

▷ maintain the security and confidentiality of the system

▷ follow procedures for dealing with obsolete/unwanted documents

▷ identify and recover overdue files

▷ trace missing files

▷ maintain, update and use circulation slips

▷ follow safety procedures at all times

BACKGROUND KNOWLEDGE

A filing system must be easy to understand and use for everyone requiring access to it.

Where a number of departments require access to the same information, a centralised filing system is often set up for the whole company and filing clerks are employed to operate the system. However, most departments also file relevant information within their own sections. To make these systems easy to understand and use, it is helpful to display a set of instructions on the current system and how to use it in a prominent place.

A locked drawer with limited access to keys should be provided in which to file all confidential documents. Confidential documents which are no longer required should be shredded and disposed of immediately.

Follow-up procedures are important in any filing system to enable files to be traced and followed up when necessary, and there are a number of ways in which this can be done.

A **files borrowed list** can be compiled, showing: date borrowed, file title, borrowed by, department, expected return date, and actual return date. This list can then be checked daily and action taken to recover files which have not been returned.

A **tickler system** can be set up to hold file issued slips. A daily tickler system contains two sets of cards, one with the names of the month and the second with the dates 1–31. When a file is lent out, the **file issued slip** is placed behind the number of the day after it was due to be returned (for example, the file issued slip for a file issued on 1 February for three days should be inserted behind 4 February).

Every day the card for that day will 'tickle' the memory of the filing clerk to recover the outstanding files. The day's card is then moved to the back of the file and the card for the next day is ready at the front of the file for action to be taken tomorrow. If a file is returned early then the file issued slip is simply removed from the tickler file and destroyed.

Circulation slips are attached to files which need to be seen by a number of people at regular intervals. The slip shows: title of document, name of person, department, date received, and date forwarded.

For example, a city council which has many committees meeting will produce circulation slips containing the names of everyone involved in each committee. When documents need to be circulated, it is a simple matter to attach the correct circulation slip and ensure that everyone sees the documents.

A copy of the circulation slip with the name of the document and the date circulated is kept on file. The document is circulated in the order of the names on the list. The final date received should be the date on which the document arrives back at the files.

Storage of information in computers is now commonplace, with storage media capable of holding as many as one million A4 documents on a single disc. The operation of these systems requires the establishment of careful labelling, filing recovery and deletion procedures, generally called housekeeping.

A **computer file** is a collection of related information and can be compared to a file folder in a vertical filing drawer. The names of your files are kept in a **directory**, which also contains information on the size of every file and the dates they were created and updated. Data management programs enable the user to store and retrieve selected information very quickly.

Computers are also used to output information directly on to microfilm (COM) instead of on to paper. This allows large quantities of hard copy to be stored in a very small space.

Unit 13, Element 1 *Process records in a database* provides opportunities for students/trainees to gain experience in handling computer files.

Confidentiality of information held in computers can be ensured by a series of passwords, which will allow entry by operators into specified areas of data. For example, the general office clerk will have a low-level password, which means the amount of information accessible to him/her is restricted, while the managing director will have a high-level password allowing him/her access to all the information held by the computer.

The Data Protection Act 1984 regulates computer data to protect the privacy of the individual. Organisations which store personal information electronically are required to register on the Data User's Register, which details the information stored, what it will be used for and who has access to it.

The Act states that data must be obtained lawfully and fairly, be adequate only for specified purposes, be accurate and up to date, and not be kept longer than is necessary. The Act provides individuals with the right to know what data is stored on them, and for what purposes the information will be used.

An individual who is adversely affected by any disclosures of information, or if the information is disclosed to unauthorised persons, may have the right to claim damages. It is the responsibility of the organisation holding the data to ensure that information is secured against misuse.

THE TASKS

Resources required by students/trainees

You will each require photocopies of the following:

▷ Task 2 – the file absent card – three copies; the file issued slip – three copies

You will also require:

▷ Task 2 – a tickler file

TASK 1

On checking your file absent record, you notice that a number of files are overdue by one week. Telephone follow-ups have been ineffective.

Draft a short form for a memorandum which could be completed and sent from the Chief Filing Clerk to the individuals concerned requesting the immediate return of the files.

TASK 2

The following files will be required by John Clooney for the Board meeting tomorrow:

J. C. Hunt & Co, 135 Avon Road, Kidderminster W30 5AT

MacDonagh & Sons, 19 Commander Close, Wakefield WA7 4DR

Redditch Sheet Metal, 13 Watling Street, Rugby RG2 9TD

John Clooney should return them within three days.

(a) Prepare a file absent card to be placed in the filing drawer for each file.

(b) Complete file issued slips for his secretary, Jane Cole, to sign when she collects the files.

(c) Put the file issued slips into a tickler file to be checked in four days' time.

TASK 3

The following tasks should if possible be completed using a computer sort.

(a) Input the following list.

(b) Rearrange the whole list into alphabetical order.

(c) Prepare alphabetical lists for each workshop.

NAME	BRANCH	WORKSHOP
Miss S. Jones	Cardiff	4
Ms H. Ohrman	Swansea	1
Mr G. Carter	Coventry	2
Miss D. Crossland	Birmingham	3
Mr J. Patnaik	Widnes	1
Mr L. Sergeant	Warrington	2
Miss K. McDermot	Wigan	3
Miss G. Anderson	Coventry	4
Mr K. Kohler	Northampton	1
Mr C. Hudson	Crewe	2
Mr H. Davenport	Cardiff	3
Miss J. Beynon	Walsall	4
Ms H. Harrison	Bilston	1
Miss G. Phillips	Newcastle	2
Mr T. Beech	Rugby	3
Ms E. Cutter	Leicester	4
Mrs C. Handay	Solihull	1
Mr J. Beesley	Coventry	2
Mr K. Dawson	Nottingham	3
Ms C. Bain	Kenilworth	4
Ms M. Williams	Warwick	1
Mr D. Payne	Melton Mowbray	2
Miss K. McCarthy	Widnes	3
Mr G. Payne	Leeds	4
Miss A. Kennedy	Leeds	1

continued ▶

continued

NAME	BRANCH	WORKSHOP
Mr L. McDermot	Bradford	2
Mr J. Smith	Castleford	3
Ms L. Smith	Whitehaven	4
Ms J. McCluskey	Sheffield	1
Ms C. Newborn	Hull	2
Mr J. Newberry	Luton	3
Mr T. Thomas	Daventry	4
Mrs A. Terry	Luton	1
Mr C. Potter	Gateshead	2
Mr A. Johnson	Birmingham	3
Mrs B. Harte	Wolverhampton	4

TASK 4

Give three reasons why it is important to destroy unwanted documents.

TASK 5

What is the procedure for dealing with files which are over one year old, but which may be needed for reference at some time in the future?

TASK 6

What is the procedure for handling confidential documents in terms of:

(a) storage?

(b) unwanted documents?

If you are also taking Unit 1 *Filing*, check that these procedures have been followed with the letter to Capt. Attwood and the memorandum to Jane Johnson.

TASK 7

The file for Johnson Bros cannot be traced. What steps should be taken?

TASK 8

What potential safety hazards are there in filing?

TASK 9

Prepare a circulation slip to be attached to the minutes of the Finance Committee Meeting held on the 30th of last month. The document is to be circulated to all members of the General Purposes Committee and should be returned to the files by the 15th of this month.

The members are:

Jenny Gardner – Accounts

Peter Jones – Finance

Harry Clare – Sales

Elizabeth Cranwell – Purchasing

Kim Parry – Accounts

Jean Laughton – Sales

Margaret Douglas – Finance

ELEMENT 12.2   *Supply information for a specific purpose*

INTRODUCTION

What do you have to do?

▷ demonstrate competence in relation to the performance criteria in Unit 1 *Filing*:

Element 1.1   *File documents and open new files within an established filing system*

Element 1.2   *Identify and retrieve documents from within an established filing system*

▷ identify and access information sources

▷ abstract all the relevant information

▷ offer alternative options when the resourced information does not match defined needs

▷ select suitable displays for the presentation of information

▷ transcribe and compile data correctly

▷ present correct data within specific time limits

What do you need to know?

▷ how to access, retrieve and present information from reference books, computer files, paper files, lists, viewdata and microfiche

▷ how to present information effectively in the form of written communications, such as memos, letters, graphs, charts and diagrams

▷ how to plan and organise your work within deadlines

What do you need to be able to do?

▷ extract information from a variety of sources

▷ present information accurately in the most suitable format

▷ provide suitable alternative information as required

▷ produce accurate information within required deadlines

▷ liaise effectively with colleagues and others

BACKGROUND KNOWLEDGE

Information is only useful if it can be retrieved quickly and accurately in a format which is easy to read and to understand. In Element 12.1 *Maintain an established filing system*, you have dealt with manual and computerised storage of information but in addition to these most companies will have a selection of reference books in the office, and you should know how to use these.

General reference books will usually consist of various dictionaries, a thesaurus, A–Z books of towns and cities, road maps, airline timetables, telephone directories, etc. Many companies have a special technical library containing sources of information relating to their particular areas of work.

Trade associations produce manuals and trade bulletins which are a good source of reference. Public libraries and private and public viewdata systems are extremely useful when researching information.

When you are asked to trace information you should make a careful note of the information required, ask questions if you do not understand, and then make a list of the steps you will take to trace the information. To avoid repeating your enquiries it is important to cross out each step as you take it.

Make a note of the answers to your queries, as this will be useful if you need to find another source for the information.

Whenever you find a new source of information you should make out a card containing the type of information and give the name, address and telephone number. The card should then be filed in your card index box.

The way in which you present the information when you have found it will depend upon the type of information you have been requested to find. A simple 'yes' or 'no' answer will probably be given orally. More detailed answers will be presented in writing to avoid errors.

Written communications may take the form of a memo, letter, graph, tabulation or diagram. You should remember to date and initial any written information you present.

THE TASKS

Resources required by students/trainees

▷ Tasks 1 and 4 – graph paper; coloured felt-tip pens

▷ Task 4 – access to filing cabinet and computer database where Business Administration details were stored in Element 12.1

TASK 1

You are required to present the following information as a bar graph:

January	£20,000	February	£19,000
March	£15,000	April	£ 6,500
May	£ 8,000	June	£25,000
July	£17,500	August	£18,500

Sales figures up to August 199–

TASK 2

Miss Jennings has a meeting in Doncaster on 20 October at 4 p.m. and another on 21 October at 9 a.m. She has asked you to find her a hotel in Doncaster which has swimming facilities. She requires a single room with en-suite facilities, dinner on 20 October and breakfast on 21 October. She would also like you to plan her route from Coventry.

(a) Give the name, address and telephone number of a suitable hotel.

(b) Give the cost of the hotel.

(c) Work out the mileage and the route, and provide a map from the motorway to the hotel.

(d) State the approximate time she should leave Coventry to allow her to arrive at the hotel by 3 p.m. at the latest.

TASK 3

Name five general reference books which you consider are essential in any office.

TASK 4

From the details you have put into your manual filing system in Element 12.1, extract the following information and present it as a bar graph; or you may prefer to present separate bar graphs for Levels I and II.

(a) Names of students/trainees.

(b) How many units each student/trainee has completed in Level I.

(c) How many units each student/trainee has completed in Level II.

(d) If you have the details on a computer database, take a printout of your own record, showing how many units, elements and tasks you have completed to date.

UNIT 13

INFORMATION PROCESSING

ELEMENT 13.1 *Process records in a database*

INTRODUCTION

What do you have to do?

▷ create, amend and delete records in a database file

▷ take a back-up copy of a database file

How well do you have to do it?

To achieve this you must be able to:

▷ correctly enter new data into an existing database

▷ back up the database to guard against loss of data

▷ deal with confidential data in a secure manner

▷ deal with simple faults and report those you cannot deal with yourself

▷ follow your workplace's/training centre's procedures for operating hardware, naming files and taking back-up copies

What do you need to know?

▷ how to use your computer, including its operating system and database package

▷ what computer files are kept and what their structure is

▷ what sort of data database programs are suitable for

What do you need to be able to do?

▷ input data correctly from paper records

▷ proof-read screen-based and printed information

▷ complete the entering of data in a reasonable time

▷ sort the records in a data file as required

▷ print the records required from a data file

▷ interpret computer manuals for both hardware and software

▷ format a floppy disc and use it to take a back-up copy of a database

▷ deal with confidential data, both on paper and on computer

BACKGROUND KNOWLEDGE

When computer files are created, their record structure is fixed in terms of the fields they will contain. Details of the fields, their type (whether alphabetic, numeric or alphanumeric – that is, text, numbers or a mixture of text and numbers), and sizes or lengths make up the **file specification**.

The program most commonly used to handle data files is called a **database program**, and it allows records in files to be entered, amended or deleted. When the database program is used to search for or sort the data, the results are output to the screen or printer in the form of a **report**.

It is very rare for a single file on its own to be a great deal of use. More often, several files are needed, each with a different structure, but with links (**relations**) between them. This group of files is called a **database**, and the program that handles them is called a **relational database**.

When data is entered into the database, creating a new record, it is usually **keyed** in using a keyboard. Sometimes typing errors occur, called **transcription** errors. Since it is very important that data files should be correct, the operator must proof-read the screen when the new record has been keyed in, but before entering the record into the data file.

Not all data has to be keyed. For example, if a customer orders ten boxes of shampoo and the computer already has the price of the shampoo in a product file, it can calculate the value of the order using a formula.

Databases are commonly used to produce printed reports, where selected records and specific fields only may be needed. Data files often need to be **sorted** into a different order to provide useful information.

The data on a disc is very precious and steps must be taken to guard against its loss. Looking after files on disc is often called **housekeeping**, and involves:

- keeping files in an orderly way by using **directories**
- preparing floppy discs to receive files by **formatting** them
- copying files onto **back-up** discs regularly
- **deleting** files no longer required

All of these tasks can be done using the **operating system** of the computer, but it is easier and safer to use the facilities from within the program wherever possible.

Your computer will have an **instruction manual**, from which you can find out how to use the operating system and database program.

Sometimes data is so private and confidential that only authorised people have access to it. Such files are usually protected by **passwords** and the computers on which these files are kept can be locked using a key. If you are given the password, do not write it down and leave it where it may be seen.

If the computer is left unattended, the room in which it is kept should also be locked. The use of personal data is covered by the Data Protection Act (see Unit 3, Element 3.3 *Update records in a computerised database*).

THE TASKS

Soft Soap Ltd (this company will be familiar to you if you took Unit 3 *Data processing*) is becoming accustomed to the use of its computer in handling its Sales and Customer files. They are finding that their initial set-up could be improved. Some of the tasks below concern the changes they would like to make to existing files, and new files and facilities they would like to add.

Resources required by students/trainees

You will each require photocopies of the following:

▷ Task 2 – one copy of the printout

You will also require:

▷ Task 7 – a calculator

APRIL	MAY	JUNE	JULY
M T W T F S S	M T W T F S S	M T W T F S S	M T W T F S S
1 2 3 4 5 6 7	1 2 3 4 5	1 2	1 2 3 4 5 6 7
8 9 10 11 12 13 14	6 7 8 9 10 11 12	3 4 5 6 7 8 9	8 9 10 11 12 13 14
15 16 17 18 19 20 21	13 14 15 16 17 18 19	10 11 12 13 14 15 16	15 16 17 18 19 20 21
22 23 24 25 26 27 28	20 21 22 23 24 25 26	17 18 19 20 21 22 23	22 23 24 25 26 27 28
29 30	27 28 29 30 31	24 25 26 27 28 29 30	29 30 31

AUGUST	SEPTEMBER	OCTOBER	NOVEMBER
M T W T F S S	M T W T F S S	M T W T F S S	M T W T F S S
1 2 3 4	1	1 2 3 4 5 6	1 2 3
5 6 7 8 9 10 11	2 3 4 5 6 7 8	7 8 9 10 11 12 13	4 5 6 7 8 9 10
12 13 14 15 16 17 18	9 10 11 12 13 14 15	14 15 16 17 18 19 20	11 12 13 14 15 16 17
19 20 21 22 23 24 25	16 17 18 19 20 21 22	21 22 23 24 25 26 27	18 19 20 21 22 23 24
26 27 28 29 30 31	23 24 25 26 27 28 29	28 29 30 31	25 26 27 28 29 30
	30		

DECEMBER	JANUARY	FEBRUARY	MARCH
M T W T F S S	M T W T F S S	M T W T F S S	M T W T F S S
1	1 2 3 4 5 6	1 2 3	1 2 3
2 3 4 5 6 7 8	7 8 9 10 11 12 13	4 5 6 7 8 9 10	4 5 6 7 8 9 10
9 10 11 12 13 14 15	14 15 16 17 18 19 20	11 12 13 14 15 16 17	11 12 13 14 15 16 17
16 17 18 19 20 21 22	21 22 23 24 25 26 27	18 19 20 21 22 23 24	18 19 20 21 22 23 24
23 24 25 26 27 28 29	28 29 30 31	25 26 27 28	25 26 27 28 29 30 31
30 31			

Diary for the year for reference purposes

TASK 1

The following file specification gives the structure of a sales transaction file, including field types and lengths. A blank record card is also shown.

Compare the sales transaction record with the record structure given in the file specification. Are they compatible?

To answer this, you need to compare them field by field and find any differences. Make a list of the differences (you should find six).

```
Sales transaction

Customer reference: _ _ _

Product code: _ _ _ _ _

Quantity: _ _ _

Date of order: __  __  __
               DD / MM / YY

Salesperson (circle): Jim/Bob/Ali/Ted/Jan
```

Blank record card

Field name	Type	Length	Description
Cust-Ref	Text	3	3 character code
Order-No	Alphanumeric	5	5 digits
Prod-No	Alphanumeric	5	1 char + 4 digits
Quantity	Numeric	3	3 digit number
Date	Date	6	Date of order
Salespers	Text	3	Choice of five names
Value	Numeric	6	Value up to £1000
Out	Text	1	Y or N
Date-Out	Date	6	Date of delivery
Paid	Text	1	Y or N
Date-Paid	Date	6	Date of payment
TOTAL		45	

File specification for a sales transaction file

TASK 2

Twelve data collection forms follow. Your tutor will give you a printout which is supposed to show the state of the records after the details on the forms have been keyed in.

(a) Check the printout against the records and identify any keying errors. (Information on how to do this correctly is to be found in Unit 3, Element 2 *Identify and mark errors on scripted material, for correction*.)

(b) Correct the printout (preferably in red) and hand it to your supervisor.

```
┌──────────────────────────────────────────────────────────────┐
│ Sales transaction                                              │
│                                                                │
│ Customer reference: H A I      Customer's order no.: 0 6 4 5 3 │
│                                                                │
│ Product code: H 0 5 0 1                                        │
│                                                                │
│ Quantity: 0 0 6              Date of order: 12   03   9-       │
│                                             ── / ── / ──       │
│                                             DD   MM   YY       │
│                                                                │
│ Salesperson (circle): Jim/(Bob)/Ali/Ted/Jan                    │
│                                                                │
│ Delivered ( (Y)/ N )         Delivery date: 15   03   9-       │
│                                             ── / ── / ──       │
│                                             DD   MM   YY       │
│                                                                │
│ Paid: ( Y / (N) )                                              │
└──────────────────────────────────────────────────────────────┘
```

```
┌──────────────────────────────────────────────────────────────┐
│ Sales transaction                                              │
│                                                                │
│ Customer reference: A C E      Customer's order no.: 2 0 2 0 3 │
│                                                                │
│ Product code: H 0 7 0 2                                        │
│                                                                │
│ Quantity: 0 1 2              Date of order: 28   03   9-       │
│                                             ── / ── / ──       │
│                                             DD   MM   YY       │
│                                                                │
│ Salesperson (circle): Jim/Bob/(Ali)/Ted/Jan                    │
│                                                                │
│ Delivered ( (Y)/ N )         Delivery date: 02   04   9-       │
│                                             ── / ── / ──       │
│                                             DD   MM   YY       │
│                                                                │
│ Paid: ( (Y) / N )                                              │
└──────────────────────────────────────────────────────────────┘
```

Data collection forms for Task 2

```
┌─────────────────────────────────────────────────────────────┐
│ Sales transaction                                             │
│                                                               │
│ Customer reference: A C E     Customer's order no.: 1 9 4 5 0 │
│                                                               │
│ Product code: C O 1 0 1                                       │
│                                                               │
│ Quantity: 0 1 5              Date of order:  14   03    9-    │
│                                              ── / ── / ──     │
│                                              DD   MM    YY    │
│                                                               │
│ Salesperson (circle): Jim/Bob/Ali/(Ted)/Jan                   │
│                                                               │
│ Delivered ( (Y)/ N )         Delivery date:  20   03    9-   │
│                                              ── / ── / ──     │
│                                              DD   MM    YY    │
│                                                               │
│ Paid: ( (Y)/ N )                                              │
└─────────────────────────────────────────────────────────────┘
```

```
┌─────────────────────────────────────────────────────────────┐
│ Sales transaction                                             │
│                                                               │
│ Customer reference: B A N     Customer's order no.: 0 0 1 9 6 │
│                                                               │
│ Product code: M 0 3 0 1                                       │
│                                                               │
│ Quantity: 0 0 1              Date of order:  17   03    9-    │
│                                              ── / ── / ──     │
│                                              DD   MM    YY    │
│                                                               │
│ Salesperson (circle): (Jim)/Bob/Ali/Ted/Jan                   │
│                                                               │
│ Delivered ( (Y)/ N )         Delivery date:  20   03    9-   │
│                                              ── / ── / ──     │
│                                              DD   MM    YY    │
│                                                               │
│ Paid: ( (Y)/ N )                                              │
└─────────────────────────────────────────────────────────────┘
```

```
┌─────────────────────────────────────────────────────────────┐
│ Sales transaction                                             │
│                                                               │
│ Customer reference: H A I     Customer's order no.: 0 6 5 4 7 │
│                                                               │
│ Product code: S 0 3 0 2                                       │
│                                                               │
│ Quantity: 0 0 2              Date of order:  16   03    9-    │
│                                              ── / ── / ──     │
│                                              DD   MM    YY    │
│                                                               │
│ Salesperson (circle): Jim/Bob/Ali/(Ted)/Jan                   │
│                                                               │
│ Delivered ( Y /(N) )         Delivery date:  __   __    __   │
│                                              ── / ── / ──     │
│                                              DD   MM    YY    │
│                                                               │
│ Paid: ( Y /(N) )                                              │
└─────────────────────────────────────────────────────────────┘
```

```
┌─────────────────────────────────────────────────────────────┐
│ Sales transaction                                             │
│                                                               │
│ Customer reference: B A N     Customer's order no.: 0 0 2 0 3 │
│                                                               │
│ Product code: S 0 3 0 1                                       │
│                                                               │
│ Quantity: 0 1 2              Date of order:  15   03    9-    │
│                                              ── / ── / ──     │
│                                              DD   MM    YY    │
│                                                               │
│ Salesperson (circle): Jim/(Bob)/Ali/Ted/Jan                   │
│                                                               │
│ Delivered ( (Y)/ N )         Delivery date:  21   03    9-   │
│                                              ── / ── / ──     │
│                                              DD   MM    YY    │
│                                                               │
│ Paid: ( Y /(N) )                                              │
└─────────────────────────────────────────────────────────────┘
```

Data collection forms for Task 2

```
┌─────────────────────────────────────────────────────────────┐
│ Sales transaction                                             │
│ Customer reference: C O S    Customer's order no.: 2 3 7 5H   │
│ Product code: H 0 7 0 2                                       │
│ Quantity: 0 1 0           Date of order:  16    03    9-      │
│                                          ───── / ───── / ──── │
│                                           DD     MM     YY    │
│                                                               │
│ Salesperson (circle): Jim/Bob/Ali/Ted/(Jan)                   │
│                                                               │
│ Delivered ( (Y)/ N )      Delivery date: 20    03    9-       │
│                                         ───── / ───── / ──── │
│                                          DD     MM     YY     │
│ Paid: ( (Y)/ N )                                              │
└─────────────────────────────────────────────────────────────┘
```

```
┌─────────────────────────────────────────────────────────────┐
│ Sales transaction                                             │
│ Customer reference: B A N    Customer's order no.: 0 0 2 0 3  │
│ Product code: H 0 7 0 1                                       │
│ Quantity: 0 1 0           Date of order:  15    03    9-      │
│                                          ───── / ───── / ──── │
│                                           DD     MM     YY    │
│                                                               │
│ Salesperson (circle): Jim/(Bob)/Ali/Ted/Jan                   │
│                                                               │
│ Delivered ( (Y)/ N )      Delivery date: 21    03    9-       │
│                                         ───── / ───── / ──── │
│                                          DD     MM     YY     │
│ Paid: ( Y / (N) )                                             │
└─────────────────────────────────────────────────────────────┘
```

```
┌─────────────────────────────────────────────────────────────┐
│ Sales transaction                                             │
│ Customer reference: P E R    Customer's order no.: P E 1 1 6  │
│ Product code: C 0 3 0 1                                       │
│ Quantity: 0 1 5           Date of order:  21    03    9-      │
│                                          ───── / ───── / ──── │
│                                           DD     MM     YY    │
│                                                               │
│ Salesperson (circle): (Jim)/Bob/Ali/Ted/Jan                   │
│                                                               │
│ Delivered ( (Y)/ N )      Delivery date: 25    03    9-       │
│                                         ───── / ───── / ──── │
│                                          DD     MM     YY     │
│ Paid: ( (Y)/ N )                                              │
└─────────────────────────────────────────────────────────────┘
```

```
┌─────────────────────────────────────────────────────────────┐
│ Sales transaction                                             │
│ Customer reference: F A I    Customer's order no.: A 6 1 7 4  │
│ Product code: C 0 2 0 1                                       │
│ Quantity: 0 1 2           Date of order:  26    03    9-      │
│                                          ───── / ───── / ──── │
│                                           DD     MM     YY    │
│                                                               │
│ Salesperson (circle): Jim/Bob/(Ali)/Ted/Jan                   │
│                                                               │
│ Delivered ( Y /(N) )      Delivery date: ── / ── / ──        │
│                                          DD   MM   YY         │
│ Paid: ( Y /(N) )                                              │
└─────────────────────────────────────────────────────────────┘
```

Data collection forms for Task 2

```
┌─────────────────────────────────────────────────────────────┐
│ ┌───────────────────────────────────────────────────────────┐ │
│ │ Sales transaction                                         │ │
│ │ Customer reference: JAN      Customer's order no.: BA937  │ │
│ │ Product code: H O 7 O I                                   │ │
│ │ Quantity: O24               Date of order: 20  03  9-     │ │
│ │                                           DD / MM / YY    │ │
│ │ Salesperson (circle): (Jim)/Bob/Ali/Ted/Jan              │ │
│ │ Delivered ( Y /(N) )        Delivery date: __ __ __      │ │
│ │                                           DD / MM / YY    │ │
│ │ Paid: ( Y /(N) )                                          │ │
│ └───────────────────────────────────────────────────────────┘ │
└─────────────────────────────────────────────────────────────┘
```

Sales transaction
Customer reference: JAN   Customer's order no.: BA937
Product code: H O 7 O I
Quantity: O24   Date of order: 20 / 03 / 9- (DD / MM / YY)
Salesperson (circle): (Jim)/Bob/Ali/Ted/Jan
Delivered (Y /(N))   Delivery date: __ / __ / __ (DD / MM / YY)
Paid: (Y /(N))

Sales transaction
Customer reference: FAI   Customer's order no.: A6 174
Product code: H O 7 O2
Quantity: O36   Date of order: 26 / 03 / 9- (DD / MM / YY)
Salesperson (circle): Jim/Bob/(Ali)/Ted/Jan
Delivered (Y /(N))   Delivery date: __ / __ / __ (DD / MM / YY)
Paid: (Y /(N))

Data collection forms for Task 2

TASK 3

Now that you have identified the errors, make the necessary amendments to the database file on the computer. Produce a printout similar to the one you were given in Task 2 to demonstrate that you have made the changes.

TASK 4

A new product file has been added to the database. The file is empty as no records have been entered yet. Use the computer to access the product file.

Either:
obtain a printout of the new file structure (you could try looking up how to do this in the program manual)

or:
get the new file structure on screen and make a copy of it on to paper.
   Your file structure details must show:

* the field names
* the field type
* the field size (length or number of digits)
* a description of the field contents
* the record size (number of characters)

TASK 5

Now that the product file has been created, all the following records can be entered.

(a) Record the time at which you started entering records.

(b) Key the records into the file, checking each one carefully on screen as soon as you have entered it.

(c) Obtain a complete copy of the product file.

(d) Record the time at which you completed part (c).

(e) Write your name and the start and end times for your data entry session on to the top of the printout.

(f) Compare your printout with the paper records. Circle any errors on your printout in red and hand it to your supervisor for checking.

New product record

Product code: S 0 3 0 1

Description: Pearl Toilet Soap (small)

Unit price: £ 5 0 · 0 0

Unit size: 2 0 0

Stock level: _ 2 7

New product record

Product code: S 0 3 0 2

Description: Pearl Toilet Soap (medium)

Unit price: £ 3 0 · 0 0

Unit size: 1 0 0

Stock level: _ 5 8

New product record

Product code: S 0 3 0 3

Description: Pearl Toilet Soap (large)

Unit price: £ 5 0 · 0 0

Unit size: 1 0 0

Stock level: _ 3 6

New product record

Product code: C 0 1 0 1

Description: Springtime Conditioner (dry) 250ml

Unit price: £ 1 5 · 0 0

Unit size: _ 1 5

Stock level: _ 8 4

New product record

Product code: C 0 2 0 1

Description: Springtime Conditioner (normal) 250ml

Unit price: £ 1 5 · 0 0

Unit size: _ 1 5

Stock level: 1 0 6

New product record

Product code: C 0 3 0 1

Description: Springtime Conditioner (greasy) 250ml

Unit price: £ 1 5 · 0 0

Unit size: _ 1 5

Stock level: _ 7 2

New product record

Product code: H 0 5 0 1

Description: Medicated Herbal Shampoo (250ml)

Unit price: £ 1 0 · 0 0

Unit size: _ 2 0

Stock level: _ 5 2

New product record

Product code: H 0 5 0 2

Description: Medicated Herbal Shampoo (500ml)

Unit price: £ 1 7 · 5 0

Unit size: _ 2 0

Stock level: _ 6 3

New product record cards for Task 5

New product record

Product code: H 0 7 0 1

Description: Springhnie Shampoo (250ml)

Unit price: £ _ 8·50

Unit size: _ 2 0

Stock level: _ 27

New product record

Product code: H 0 7 0 2

Description: Springhnie Shampoo (500ml)

Unit price: £ 1 5·00

Unit size: _ 2 0

Stock level: _ 3 4

New product record

Product code: M 0 1 0 1

Description: Super Mousse - Styling

Unit price: £ 1 0·0 0

Unit size: _ 1 5

Stock level: _ 1 4

New product record

Product code: M 0 2 0 1

Description: Super Tinting Mousse - Blonde

Unit price: £ 1 0·0 0

Unit size: _ 1 5

Stock level: _ 1 2

New product record

Product code: M 0 4 0 1

Description: Super Tinting Mousse - Redhead

Unit price: £ 1 0·0 0

Unit size: _ 1 5

Stock level: _ 1 4

New product record

Product code: M 0 3 0 1

Description: Super Tinting Mousse - Brunette

Unit price: £ 1 0·0 0

Unit size: _ 1 5

Stock level: _ 1 7

New product record cards for Task 5

TASK 6   Ask your tutor for a blank floppy disc. Format the disc and copy the newly created product file on to it.

TASK 7
(a) Obtain a listing of the new product file showing only the product number, the unit price and unit size. Try and get your printout in columns, sorted in the order of product code.

(b) You need to know the value of all the goods on order which have been delivered but which have not yet been paid for, sorted by customer.

(i) List only those records from the sales transaction file with Out set to Y and with Paid set to N. The listing should be in alphabetical order by customer.

(ii) Now you need to find the total of all the value fields for the records you located in part (b) (i). You may be able to get your computer to do this. If not, just use your printout from part (b) (i) and a calculator to obtain a total for the value field for all the records.

ELEMENT 13.2 *Process information in spreadsheets*

INTRODUCTION

What do you have to do?

▷ enter data into new or existing computer-based spreadsheets

▷ make projections of future figures

▷ take a back-up copy of a spreadsheet

▷ delete a spreadsheet

How well do you have to do it?

To achieve this you must be able to:

▷ enter new data correctly into an existing spreadsheet

▷ set up a new spreadsheet to store text, numbers and formulas

▷ project future figures from existing figures and expected trends

▷ back up the spreadsheet to guard against loss of data

▷ deal with confidential data in a secure manner

▷ deal with simple faults and report those you cannot deal with yourself

▷ follow your workplace's/training centre's procedures for operating hardware, naming files and taking back-up copies

What do you need to know?

▷ how to use your computer, including its operating system and spreadsheet package and their manuals

▷ what spreadsheets are kept, and what their structure is

▷ what sort of data spreadsheets are suitable for

What do you need to be able to do?

▷ input data correctly from paper records

▷ proof-read screen-based and printed information

▷ complete the entering of data in a reasonable time

▷ sort the rows in a spreadsheet as required

▷ print all or part of a spreadsheet

▷ interpret computer manuals for both hardware and software

▷ format a floppy disc and use it to take a back-up copy of a spreadsheet

▷ deal with confidential data, both on paper and on computer

BACKGROUND KNOWLEDGE

Spreadsheets kept on computer systems are equivalent to paper spreadsheets, on which **rows** and **columns** of figures are recorded, totalled and reconciled. The advantage of using a computer is that changes to any of the figures will result in a change being made automatically to the totals figure.

Each position on the spreadsheet into which a figure can be placed is identified by its row and column number, and is known as a **cell**.

Where figures are totalled, or some other calculation performed, the result is determined by a **formula** which is given to the computer by the operator. Formulas can be stored along with the figures when the spreadsheet is saved to disc.

Normally, **overtyping** any of the figures on the spreadsheet causes **automatic** recalculation of the formulas, although this facility can be switched off.

Often a spreadsheet will need to be used again and again with different figures. In these cases, the spreadsheet should be loaded and the figures entered, and then the spreadsheet saved under a new name. This leaves the original spreadsheet unchanged on disc.

Whole spreadsheets can be printed, or certain areas selected for printing. It is quite common for spreadsheets to be wider than your printer paper, so unless you have a wide carriage printer, your printout may well cover several page widths in normal printing. You will need either to piece it together when it is all printed, or to use condensed printing to fit more on to the page.

Spreadsheets are often used to handle financial information important to the running of a company. In particular, they are often used for **what if** predictions. For example, a manager might use a spreadsheet to predict what the company's profit would be if sales increased by a certain percentage each month.

Such forecasts are highly confidential, and access to spreadsheets on disc should be limited to authorised personnel. Printouts should not be left lying around but should be given to the person who requires them, or filed away securely, as soon as they are produced.

THE TASKS

Soft Soap Ltd (see Unit 3, Element 3 *Update records in a computerised database*, and Unit 13, Element 13.1 *Process records in a database*) uses a spreadsheet program for two main tasks. The stationery supervisor keeps a record of the stationery stock on a spreadsheet and the accounts department calculates wages for salespeople on a spreadsheet.

Resources required by students/trainees

You will each require photocopies of the following:

▷ Task 1 – the eight requisition forms – one copy; the blank order form – one copy

▷ Task 2 – the delivery note – one copy

▷ Task 4 – the rough wages chart – one copy

TASK 1

The stationery supervisor of Soft Soap Ltd uses a spreadsheet called SSTOCK. She receives requisitions for stationery daily from other departments. She keys the details of each requisition into her spreadsheet, and when they have all been processed, she prints out a copy of the spreadsheet to check if any reordering needs to be done.

(a) Ask your tutor for a batch of requisitions. Key one requisition at a time into the Requisition column of the SSTOCK spreadsheet. Your stock level should update as you go along, so when you finish one requisition and go on to the next one, you can simply overtype the previous details. When all have been entered, fill the Requisition column with zeros before printing and saving.

(b) Produce a printout of the spreadsheet and underline in red the items that need reordering.

(c) Type or wordprocess an order to Harris Stationery Supplies, 47 Station Road, Fairtown FB7 2JB, for the items that need reordering. Your tutor will give you an order form.

TASK 2

Stationery deliveries come in each week. From the delivery note which your supervisor will give you, key the details into the Delivery column of the SSTOCK spreadsheet and print out a copy. Change the Delivery column back to zeros when you have finished printing and before saving the spreadsheet.

TASK 3

Using the sales transaction file from Unit 13 Element 13.1 (page 22), produce a printout from the file showing only the fields for salesperson, product code, delivery date and value. The records you print out should be for the month of March, and should show only sales that were delivered during that month.

TASK 4

The gross pay of the sales personnel is based on their basic pay plus commission on the deliveries made. For each salesperson, use the printout from Task 3 and do a rough calculation of his/her likely gross pay. Record it on the rough wages chart which your tutor will give you. In fact, the rate of commission varies from product to product, but you can take 10 per cent as a working average.

The spreadsheet called WAGES allows you to work out the exact gross pay of the sales personnel. Use the printout from Task 3 and the basic wage shown on the rough wages chart from Task 4.

Load WAGES, and for each salesperson in turn, type in:

- his/her name
- his/her basic wage
- his/her sales of each product for the month of March

Save the results for each salesperson as you complete them. Save them under his/her name (as BOB, JAN, etc.). For each one, produce a printout showing just rows 1 to 5. Check your printouts against the rough calculations for Task 4 and make sure there are no big discrepancies. If there are, go back and find out where you went wrong.

ELEMENT 13.3 *Access and print hard copy reports, summaries and documents*

INTRODUCTION

What do you have to do?

▷ produce printed output in the required format from a computer system

▷ operate a printer, including carrying out routine maintenance tasks

How well do you have to do it?

To achieve this you must be able to:

▷ prepare the printer with the correct paper and settings

▷ produce printouts from various types of software to the specification required

▷ deal with simple printer faults and report those you cannot deal with yourself

What do you need to know?

▷ what sorts of printer are commonly found in the workplace

▷ what kinds of paper they can handle

▷ what print styles are available

▷ how to operate your printer

What do you need to be able to do?

▷ operate your printer correctly, including changing the paper, clearing a paper jam, changing the printer ribbon/toner or ink cartridge

▷ collate work and distribute it correctly

▷ deal with confidential printouts sensitively

▷ produce printouts which conform to the specification required in terms of the data shown, the format and the paper

BACKGROUND KNOWLEDGE

Your workplace/training centre may have one or more of a number of different types of printer. They are used to produce **hard copy**, which can be taken away and referred to as necessary. The most common printers are the **dot-matrix**, the **daisy-wheel**, the **ink-jet** and the **laser** printer.

The first three of these are **character** printers; they print one character at a time. They have a **print head** which, in the case of the daisy-wheel, can be changed to provide different character styles or **fonts** and font sizes. With the dot-matrix and ink-jet, different fonts can be produced automatically. These two types of printer can also produce **graphics**, such as graphs and pictures.

The characters are formed on the paper by the print head pressing on it through an inked **ribbon**. In the case of an ink-jet, the paper is electronically charged in the shape of the character and the ink is squirted at it. The paper is fed round the **platten** either by friction (as in a typewriter), or by **sprocket wheels**, which need paper with sprocket holes in the sides.

The paper can be **cut-sheet**, **fan-folded**, **letter-headed** or **pre-printed** (such as orders and invoices). It can be placed in the printer in **portrait** (upright) or **landscape** (sideways) mode, providing the **carriage** is wide enough. Fan-folded paper has to have the sides torn off and be separated before it is sent off. This is called **decollating**. Fan-folded printouts should not really be sent out unless this has been done. Most printing takes place on A4 paper (11.69" long and 8.25" wide), although you may use printer paper, which is 11" long and 8.5" wide, or A5 (half the size of A4).

Most printers have buttons on the top or front which allow you to switch them off (**on/off line**) without losing any of your printing. You can also feed the paper through a line at a time (**line feed**) or a page at a time (**form feed**). You may also be able to change the font, or to select **condensed** (very small) print.

Some printers (chiefly dot-matrix and ink-jet) can print in **letter** or **near-letter quality (NLQ)** and in **draft** (rough) form. Others, such as daisy-wheel or laser printer, only produce high quality documents.

Laser printers are different in many ways. They print a page at a time, so they can often print between six and fourteen pages a minute of very high quality. They are rather like photocopiers. They need special cartridges of black ink called **toner**, rather than ribbons, and have no print head or platten. They are, of course, more expensive.

THE TASKS

The printers used by your workplace/training centre will vary, so you will need to interpret the set tasks to suit your printer.

TASK 1

Demonstrate that you can:

(a) Switch your printer on and off line.

(b) Feed the paper through a line at a time.

(c) Do a form feed.

(d) Change paper type – for example, from fan-folded to cut-sheet and back again, or from plain to letter-headed and back again.

(e) Change the ribbon on your printer, or change the ink or toner cartridge.

(f) Change the font type/size on your printer (for printers such as a daisy-wheel); or set a different font type/size on the printer itself (for printers such as a dot-matrix); or set a different font type/size from your software package (for instance, from a wordprocessing program).

(g) Change from portrait to landscape printing, if you have a wide carriage printer or a laser printer with this facility.

TASK 2

From the list below, choose two different items and produce the relevant printouts:

(a) a high quality letter on letter-headed paper

(b) a printout from a spreadsheet (draft quality if possible)

(c) a landscape printout from a spreadsheet, letter quality, in a small font size (such as condensed, or 8 or 10 pitch)

(d) a listing from a database in columns (draft if possible)

(e) an envelope or sticky label

(f) a graph (pie, line or bar chart) from your spreadsheet program

This task should be repeated on four separate occasions. Record the date each time you do Task 2.

UNIT 14

TELECOMMUNICATIONS & DATA TRANSMISSION

ELEMENT 14.1 *Process incoming and outgoing telephone calls using a multiline or switchboard system*

INTRODUCTION

What do you have to do?

▷ process incoming and outgoing telephone calls using a multiline or switchboard system

How well do you have to do it?

To achieve this you must be able to:

▷ answer calls promptly and clearly in an agreed 'house' style

▷ identify callers and find out their needs

▷ transfer incoming calls to the person concerned or take and pass on messages promptly

▷ obtain external calls correctly and make contact with the person required before connecting the caller

▷ offer alternative options if requests cannot be met

▷ be courteous and helpful

▷ describe faults and promptly report them

▷ follow operating and safety procedures at all times

What do you need to know?

▷ the structure, location and responsibilities of people in your organisation; its policy on telephone calls

▷ the facilities of the system and how to operate it

▷ the procedures for passing on information

▷ how to make full use of BT services, including costs, codes and the content of directories

▷ how to communicate effectively with other members of staff and outside contacts

▷ the procedures for dealing with: faults; routine cleaning and hygiene of equipment; security; safety and emergencies

▷ how to make international calls

What do you need to be able to do?

▷ use directories and operating manuals

▷ operate a multiline or switchboard system

▷ speak clearly and communicate effectively

▷ listen actively to and interpret information

▷ check callers' needs and connect internal lines correctly

▷ transfer calls to alternative extensions, giving reasons for any delay

▷ record and transmit messages accurately

▷ assist colleagues and clients with requests and complaints

▷ write legible, logical messages

▷ follow company/organisation policy and procedures on security, safety and emergencies

▷ describe and report switchboard faults

▷ carry out routine cleaning of equipment

BACKGROUND KNOWLEDGE

The work in this unit builds on the knowledge and skills acquired in Unit 2 *Communicating information*. The assessment should preferably be carried out in the workplace over a period of time, but where this is not possible, the tasks which follow may prove helpful.

When operating a switchboard system you may be dealing with several lines at once, so additional skills are required. Like fax and telex machines, switchboards vary, and you need to become familiar with the one in your workplace/training centre so that you can operate it confidently. On many occasions it may be difficult to locate the person the caller wishes to contact; and yet at the same time you will also need to deal with the other external and internal calls.

It is important to remain calm even at the busiest times and to remind the callers politely that you are doing everything possible to connect them. It is ineffective to return rudeness to difficult callers, and surprising how some will change their attitude when confronted with politeness.

In the event of not being able to connect the caller to the appropriate person or section, you must offer to take a message and ensure that this is passed on as quickly as possible.

Each firm/organisation has its own way of answering a call. This usually takes the form of the firm's/organisation's name, followed by 'Good morning/Good afternoon, can I help you?'

When phoning you must know exactly what you want to say. Do not leave anything to chance, thinking that you will be able to remember it all. Write down all the important points and cross the information through as you cover each point. Your notes could be kept as a record as, unlike a letter or memo, there is no written record of a telephone conversation.

Many people are surprised when they hear a recording of their voice for the first time. Although you may be skilled in using the telephone at home it is a rather different situation when making a business call to a person you have never met, and prolonged pauses can give a bad impression. Remember the caller cannot see you, and s/he has only a voice to relate to. Try to have a friendly voice, not one that could seem abrasive.

As a telephonist you are the ambassador of the firm/organisation – the caller may judge the business by your efficiency.

THE TASKS

Resources required by students/trainees

You will each require photocopies of the following:

▷ Task 2 – the order form – one copy

▷ Task 3 – the blank memo – one copy

TASK 1

The following four notices are always displayed by the switchboard:

Telephone Extension Nos

Managing Director	Ms Margaret Poole	800
Accounts	Mr Alan Naylor	852
Personnel	Mrs Gillian Deane	850
Research/Marketing	Miss Ruth Gregory	863
Health and Safety	Mr William Taylor	858
Sales	Mr Brian Prescott	853
Purchasing	Mr Mahmood Zaman	851

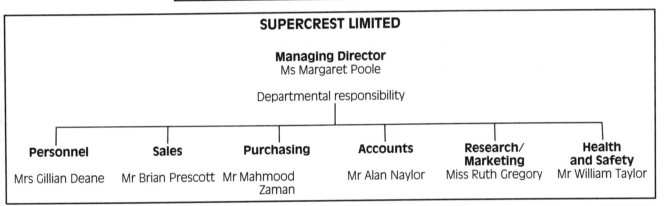

SUPERCREST LIMITED

Managing Director
Ms Margaret Poole

Departmental responsibility

Personnel	Sales	Purchasing	Accounts	Research/ Marketing	Health and Safety
Mrs Gillian Deane	Mr Brian Prescott	Mr Mahmood Zaman	Mr Alan Naylor	Miss Ruth Gregory	Mr William Taylor

IN CASE OF FIRE:
- When alarm bell rings vacate the building by the advised route, closing all doors behind you, and assemble in the car park.
- Do *not* use the lifts.
- Each section leader is to be responsible for his/her staff.
- Do *not* return to the building until instructed to do so by the Health and Safety Officer.

CONFIDENTIALITY *must* be maintained at all times.
- Do *not* discuss the company's affairs with members of the public.
- If you overhear or see anything of a confidential nature do *not* repeat the incident to anyone.
- *Never* disclose information regarding members of staff to enquirers unless instructed to do so.

(a) You are the telephonist at Supercrest Limited. The telephone has been reasonably quiet all morning. At 11.47 you answer an outside call and are told that a bomb has been placed on the premises and is due to detonate at 12.00 noon. You are taken completely by surprise and before you can ask any questions the caller rings off.
   What would you do, and in what order?

(b) You answer the telephone: 'Supercrest Limited. Can I help you?'
   'Yes, I hope so', is the reply. 'Have you a Mr Prescott working at Supercrest?'
   'Do you mean Mr Brian Prescott, the Sales Manager?'
   'Yes, I think that is the person', says the woman caller.
   'I'll put you through to his office'.
   The caller says, 'Just a minute, I would prefer to have Mr Prescott's home address and his telephone number. I've looked in the local

telephone directory as I believe he lives in the Carlton area of the town, but I cannot find any B. Prescott and I can only assume he is an ex-directory customer.'

What would you do if confronted with this situation?

(c) You have just put a call through to Mr Naylor, Accounts. Mr Naylor rings back to the switchboard to say that Mrs Crompton has been put through to the wrong extension. She wanted to speak to Mr Taylor. Mr Naylor sounded annoyed.

As this was your fault, what would you do, and what would you say to the parties concerned?

TASK 2

By simulation, using two telephone extensions and working in pairs, carry out the following telephone ordering and sales technique.

- One student/trainee is to make the call.
- One student/trainee is to receive the call and make out the order.

The student/trainee making the call will need to refer to the information on the advertisement below – the requirements are circled – and, prior to making the call, adequately prepare the message including the name, address and telephone number. The credit card no. is 2143 765 908 123.

The student/trainee receiving the call is employed by the Betterbulb Company of Spalding, Lincolnshire, telephone number 0775 23517, and will complete the order form provided. There is no need to calculate the total of the order, only the individual items, as this will be passed on and dealt with by another department.

APRIL/MAY FLOWERING TULIPS MIXED
April/May Flowering Tulips Mixed. Our exciting rainbow mixture of sturdy tulips which will provide a spectacle from mid-April and throughout May.

K29 Top Size Bulbs (11–12 cms.) for exhibition quality flowers. *(200 needed)*
   50 for £5.35   100 for £9.50

K30 First Size Bulbs (10–11 cms.) for mass planting for cut flowers.
   100 for £7.25   200 for £12.95

K35 Double Early Tulips Mixed
Many glorious varieties. Ht. 10″–12″. Fl. April/May.
   30 for £4.40   60 for £7.80

K34 Lily Flowered Tulips Mixed
So graceful and elegant, good for cutting. Ht. 22″–24″. Fl. May.
   25 for £3.50   50 for £5.95

K49 30 Apricot Beauty £5.00 *(90 needed)*
A delicious colour. This very long flowering beauty has, from being one of the most expensive tulips, become within reach of the average gardener. Ht. 16″. Fl. April/May. Top Size 11–12 cms. bulbs.

K4 Tete-a-Tete Multiheaded Dwarf Daffodils
Flowers end of February–April. Ht. 8″. With modern techniques this variety has built up stocks so that from being one of the most expensive varieties it is now excellent value. Can be grown indoors for early flowering.
   30 for £4.00

K21 Single Snowdrops
The much loved traditional small Snowdrop. Ht. 4″–5″. Fl. Feb/March.
   50 for £2.10   100 for £3.70

K19 Winter Aconites
4–5 cms. Flowering very early as with Snowdrops and Iris Reticulata.
   50 for £2.50   100 for £4.30

K22 Giant Trumpet Daffodils Unsurpassable
Unrivalled for size of bloom. An enormous trumpet from March. Top Size bulbs (12–15 cms. circ.). *(200 needed)*
   30 for £3.10   100 for £8.75

K23 Daffodils & Narcissi Mixed
Over 10 varieties go into our mixture. Top Size bulbs (12–15 cms. circ.).
   50 for £4.75   100 for £8.35

K24 Daffodils & Narcissi
Naturalising mixture. A blended mixture of many varieties as lifted from the field with large and small bulbs included. An economic way to buy for mass planting where 80%–90% will flower in the first spring. Up to 200 bulbs per 14lbs.
   14lbs £7.35   28lbs £12.95

K50 Mini collection of Rockery Daffodils £6.15
50 Bulbs – 10 each of the following 5 varieties:
   Jumblie – Ht. 8″
   Jack Snipe – Ht. 8″
   Hawera – Ht. 7″
   Minnow – Ht. 6″
   Canaliculatus – Ht. 6″
They flower from March well into April.

K51 Mixed Rockery Daffodils
A mixture from a selection of up to 20 varieties.
   30 for £3.50   60 for £5.95

TASK 3

You are Andrew Kershaw, a clerk in the Customer Services Department of Martin Taylor & Co. Ltd, clothing manufacturers. Your boss, Mr B. Crossley, is away for three days at a clothing trade fair and has left instructions for him to be notified of any urgent matters on his answering machine at home.
The organisation of Martin Taylor & Co. Ltd is set out below.

Managing Director
Miss M. Ratcliffe

Departmental responsibility

Office Services	Personnel	Accounts	Customer Services	Production	Stores and Transport
Mrs M. Govan	Miss D. Roper	Mr Y. Sheth	Mr B. Crossley	Mr M. Tate	Mr K. Dixon

You have the following telephone conversation with Mr W. Barker of Jeans for Teens Ltd, an important wholesale customer:

Clerk: Hello.

Customer: This is Mr Barker of Jeans for Teens. Who is that speaking please?

Clerk: Andrew Kershaw.

Customer: But who are you? What department am I speaking to? I asked the switchboard operator to put me through to Mr Crossley.

Clerk: Oh, I see, well he's not here. Can I help?

Customer: Well I don't know. It depends whether you know anything about my order for jeans.

Clerk: Oh probably, I know all that goes on in Customer Services.

Customer: So you work in Customer Services, you didn't say what your job was. Well I'm very annoyed with someone at your firm. We've just had a consignment of jeans delivered and find there are 100 pairs missing. What can you do about it?

Clerk: I see, Mr Parker. What was the firm's name again?

Customer: It's Barker not Parker, of Jeans for Teens. I am going to get even more annoyed in a minute. Will you please find out what has happened? I have promised a retailer delivery of the jeans that are missing and she is pressurising me, as she is turning away business, and she's a good customer of mine and I can't afford to lose her order.

Clerk: Just hang on and I'll look it up.

Customer: Well hurry please, I have an appointment in five minutes.

Clerk: (*After a pause of three minutes*) Found the order. Oh, it's Mr Crossley's fault. Yes, you ordered 600 but he's read it as 500. What a mess he's made of this. Just wait till he comes back from his trade fair. I'll enjoy telling him about his mistake.

Customer: Look, you're wasting my time. I want some action and the 100 pairs of jeans here by tomorrow morning. I don't care that Mr Crossley is away, or whose fault it is. All I want are the jeans I ordered. If they are not here by 10 o'clock tomorrow morning I'll take my business elsewhere.

Clerk: Sorry you feel like that, Mr Parker. I'm doing my best.

Customer: It's Barker not Parker. How many times do I have to tell you? Just sort it out and ring my secretary. I want to know the outcome as soon as possible. Goodbye.

Clerk: Will do. Bye!

(a) Rewrite the telephone conversation on the previous page, bearing in mind your company's image, customer relations and policy on disclosure of information.

(b) *Work in pairs*
Compare your scripts and ideas on how both of you would have dealt with the situation. Be prepared to criticise each other's amended version and alter as necessary. When you are completely satisfied with your efforts show the script to your tutor and ask for his/her opinion. Take note of any amendments suggested and finalise your script accordingly.

(c) *Work in pairs*
Using a recording/playback machine (decide your role – either clerk or customer), record the preferred version of the telephone conversation. Play back your efforts, and if you are not satisfied alter accordingly and re-record until you feel no further improvement can be made.

(d) *Group activity*
Write down the steps you would take so that Mr Barker receives his goods tomorrow morning. It would be necessary for you to contact other people in your organisation who could authorise the request for the jeans to be delivered to Jeans for Teens Ltd.

Individually
(e) Now plan your own telephone call to Mr Barker's secretary when you know what action is to be taken.

(f) Draft a memo to be sent, either by electronic mail or by hand, to the Transport Department warning them of the urgency of delivering 100 pairs of jeans to Jeans for Teens Ltd as soon as they are received by them, either later today or first thing tomorrow morning at the latest.

(g) Plan your own message for Mr Crossley's answering machine.

ELEMENT 14.2   *Transmit and transcribe recorded messages*

INTRODUCTION

What do you have to do?

▷ transmit and transcribe recorded messages

How well do you have to do it?

To achieve this you must be able to:

▷ transmit and transcribe recorded messages accurately

▷ give priority to urgent messages

▷ pass on messages promptly to the person or department concerned

▷ compose and record timed announcements giving accurate information and instructions

▷ identify faults and promptly report them

▷ follow operating and safety procedures at all times

What do you need to know?

▷ how to operate the answering machine equipment safely

▷ the structure of your organisation, and the location and responsibilities of people in it

▷ how to interpret written instructions in manuals

What do you need to be able to do?

▷ use the operating manuals

▷ operate the answering machine equipment:
- incoming:
  set answering machine to receive calls automatically
  play back recorded messages
  listen actively to and interpret information received
  identify urgent messages
  compose and record messages accurately, logically and legibly
  pass messages to the correct person promptly
  erase tape ready for reuse
  reset system to manual operation
  identify and report answering machine faults
- outgoing:
  compose and record timed announcements giving accurate information and instructions
  speak clearly

BACKGROUND KNOWLEDGE

Ideally, this unit should be undertaken in the workplace. However, the following material has been devised to help students/trainees to carry out simulation tasks/assignment in the training centre, and could also be used before going on work placement or as a reinforcement.

A telephone answering machine enables calls to be recorded either when the staff are out of the building or after business hours.

When a caller dials the required number a pre-recorded timed announcement is played. An example might be as follows:

'Hello, this is Louise Brendon speaking. I'm sorry that I can't come to the phone just now. If you will leave your name and telephone number I will return your call as soon as possible. Do not start to speak until after the sound of the tone. Should the bleep sound for 10 seconds, your message will not be recorded. In this case please call back tomorrow.'

You leave your message, and replace your receiver. The telephone answering machine is ready for the next caller. A bleep will sound for a stated number of seconds if the answering machine tape is full.

Many people feel uneasy or embarrassed talking into a machine as there is no one at the other end to respond – you are in effect talking to yourself. Therefore if you are taken aback when a machine answers a call you are making, you may wish to ring off, prepare carefully the message you are going to leave, and phone back again in order to leave it.

Many small businesses (such as the sole trader in Task 2) find the telephone answering machine a boon, as it prevents them from losing custom if they are out or busy elsewhere. You may even have experienced using the telephone answering machine when phoning a doctor or dentist, when the pre-recorded message tells you to ring another number for assistance.

Nowadays many domestic users who lead busy lives also have a telephone answering machine.

You must listen intently when the tape is played back and complete a message form with the information as you would for an ordinary telephone call, and, of course, pass on the messages to the correct people as quickly as possible. Also, you must be able to decide which messages should have priority.

When you are sure all the information has been dealt with you may erase the messages from the machine.

There are several telephone answering machines on the market at the present time and they may be bought or rented, depending on the preference of the user. If a machine that is rented develops a fault, notify the supplier, and someone will come out to repair it immediately.

Some answering machines have extra facilities such as 'Remote Access'. This will enable you to listen to your messages when you are away from the office or home; and if you forget to switch on your machine, this can be remedied by using your 'Remote Switch On' facility from any telephone.

THE TASKS

**Resources required
by students/trainees**

▷ Tasks 1 and 2 – cassette with message from Mr Smith (Task 1 (a)) and four other messages (Task 2)

▷ Task 2 – four message forms each

TASK 1

(a) Recently there has been a spate of burglaries in the district where you live and your parents are considering having a burglar alarm system installed. Your father telephones a reputable installer only to find he is expected to leave a message on an answering machine. After four days your father begins to wonder why the installer has not been in touch with him. Listen to the recording and then tell your tutor why your father was not contacted and what he should have done to make sure all information was given.

(b) A relative has promised that s/he will pay for 20 driving lessons as your birthday present. You are very pleased about this and you telephone the driving instructor immediately, only to find you are connected to an answering machine.

   Make sure that *your* message is clear and covers all the important points so that the driving instructor will understand your message and be able to give an answer immediately when s/he contacts you.

   Play back the recorded message for yourself first. If satisfied, find a partner to work with in your group, listen to your messages together and jointly try to improve them.

(c) You are 18 years of age and thinking of joining an evening class at your local college. You know from experience that you must enrol early to guarantee a place on the course. It is the week prior to official enrolment and as the staff are still on holiday an answering machine has been installed especially for enquiries.

   Record your message and play it back for your own satisfaction. Find a partner to work with in your group, listen to your messages together and jointly try to improve them.

TASK 2

Turner Maintenance & Repairs
Irlam
Manchester M30 4AT

You will be given a recording of messages received on the answering machine of the above firm while you were out at the bank. Using message forms transcribe the recorded messages accurately, logically and legibly. Then number the messages in the order of priority in which you think Mr Turner should deal with them when he returns.

ELEMENT 14.3 *Transmit and receive copies of documents electronically*

INTRODUCTION

What do you have to do?

▷ send and receive documents using a telex machine, facsimile machine or electronic mail

How well do you have to do it?

To achieve this you must be able to:

▷ accurately send and receive documents nationally and internationally

▷ deal with simple problems such as wrongly sent or received transmissions or poor quality documents

▷ ensure that documents reach the correct destination/person

▷ log work done promptly and correctly

▷ identify faults and report them promptly

▷ follow operating and safety procedures at all times

What do you need to know?

▷ the operation and care of telex and facsimile machinery

▷ how to use electronic mail

▷ the relative costs of different forms of electronic transmission of documents

▷ the logging procedures of your workplace/training centre

▷ how to find telex/facsimile numbers

What do you need to be able to do?

▷ send and receive documents of varying lengths as required

▷ log work you have sent/received

▷ identify problems with documents or equipment and deal with them or report them

▷ repeat incoming or outgoing transmissions if required

BACKGROUND KNOWLEDGE

All organisations have to deal with information on paper and to ensure that such information reaches the people who need it in time to be useful.

Conventional methods of moving paper from place to place (such as internal mail or postal systems) are usually rather slow, particularly on an international scale. Alternatives such as telex have been available for some time, but have limited flexibility. Modern, much faster methods such as facsimile and electronic mail depend on a worldwide communications system based on existing telephone networks, which use satellites for international transmissions.

The main costs involved are for equipment leasing and maintenance, operator time and, most importantly, charges for telephone time. It follows that the more quickly transmission can take place, the cheaper it will probably be to send the message.

Telex is a worldwide telecommunications network by which typed messages at one location can be received very quickly at another. A special telex machine is needed as well as a reserved phone line for the transfer of messages.

Only upper case (capital) letters are normally available on the keyboard, although simple wordprocessing functions such as insert, delete etc. are often provided by the machine.

The message needs to be typed and checked on a display or on paper before transmission. Each subscriber has a number and an answerback code which is a shortened version of his/her name. Frequently used numbers can be stored and called up using a short code. When you send a telex, the receiver sends back his/her answerback code so that you can check that the telex is going to the correct destination.

Messages can be sent as they are being typed, or stored in the memory of the telex machine for transmission later. Outgoing messages are normally printed in red on your machine but in black on the receiving machine. This helps you to tell which machine is producing the text. Incoming messages can be stored in the memory if the telex is in use. They can also be redirected to another recipient to save being retyped.

Telex directories, both national and international, can be used to look up subscribers' numbers, or you can ring the operator on 100 to make an enquiry.

When a telex has been sent or received, a copy is normally filed in sequential order and a log sheet completed with the details.

Telexes cannot cope with anything other than text or numbers, and information from the original document has to be retyped onto the telex machine. They cannot deal with graphs, diagrams, photographs or pictures.

Facsimile (fax) machines do not have text-processing facilities, but can take an existing document on paper and electronically transmit a copy of the document to another facsimile transceiver anywhere in the world. The received document is printed on heat-sensitive paper, which can fade if left exposed to light. All subscribers have their own fax number, which can be obtained by ringing 153. Group 2 machines take 2–3 minutes to send a page; newer Group 3 machines take about 20 seconds; the latest Group 4 faxes take 3–4 seconds. Most machines can transmit to any other, but at the operating speed of the slower one.

The transmitted document usually has a header sheet added to it with details of the sender, who it is for, the date and number of pages. This allows the receiver to deal with the incoming fax promptly and correctly.

The quality of the received document is usually not quite as good as the original, particularly if there are fine drawings or small text. A slower speed can be used (fine mode transmission) or a copy can be made before transmission on your own fax to see what the receiver will actually get.

The fax machine logs all calls and prints an activity report periodically, or on request. It is common for the originals of faxed documents to be returned to the originator as a confirmation that the fax has been sent and/or for copies of faxes to be filed.

Because facsimile machines deal with original documents, they can cope with any printed material A5, A4 or even A3 size, providing the text/graphics are in black and white.

Electronic mail uses personal computer technology to prepare and send documents in electronic form. Some systems operate internally only and are used for internal post (such as memos etc. within the limits of one building or company). Others allow you to mail messages to other subscribers to the system (for example, British Telecom Gold or Prestel).

Such systems normally use a modem and telephone line to make the connection to the recipient or to another computer which stores messages until they can be collected. Subscribers to an electronic mail system have a personal ID which identifies their mailbox, and entry to their mail is protected by a password.

Text to be sent can be prepared using an electronic mail program or a wordprocessing program, but the transmission of the document/message normally requires an electronic mail program. Messages are sent and received entirely in electronic form, and may never be printed, although both sender and receiver can choose to print a copy for their files should they so wish. Incoming mail can be edited and sent on to another recipient; it can be stored on disc or thrown away as required.

The program can also store mailing lists to which a copy of a message can be sent on request. Some programs allow the sender to broadcast (send a message to all users) although this is usually only practicable on internal systems.

Electronic mail offers a very useful alternative to the telephone, particularly where the recipient is likely to be out. The person's mail can wait until it can be dealt with on his/her return.

Most electronic mail systems deal only with typed text, although there are some which can send electronically prepared text/graphics documents across the world.

THE TASK

Resources required by students/trainees

You will each require photocopies of the following:

▷ The log for transmitting documents – one copy

▷ The log for receiving documents – one copy

You will need to send at least five documents and receive five documents on at least two occasions, and on at least two systems. In order to be sure that you have done this, it is a good idea to keep a log and fill it in on each occasion that you send and receive an electronic transmission.

Keep a copy of each document as proof of your work.

UNIT 15

ELEMENT 15.1 *Receive and direct visitors*

RECEPTION

INTRODUCTION

What do you have to do?

▷ receive all visitors to your organisation

▷ find out their individual needs

▷ respond in accordance with organisational policy

▷ keep all records up to date, legibly and accurately

▷ record all messages accurately and pass them on promptly and to the correct location

▷ follow security and safety procedures at all times

How well do you have to do it?

To achieve this you must be able to:

▷ welcome visitors to your organisation in a businesslike manner

▷ find out what each visitor needs

▷ direct the visitor to the appropriate person

▷ keep the visitor informed of any delays which may occur

▷ keep confidential information to yourself

▷ take messages and record them correctly

▷ pass messages on to the appropriate people

▷ deal with the following: callers without appointments, callers with both urgent and non-urgent needs, callers who are late/early for appointments, callers who require baggage or belongings to be cared for, deliveries to be received

▷ handle emergency situations

What do you need to know?

▷ how your organisation works

▷ where people are located and the layout of the building(s)

▷ how to deal with various types of caller, as listed above

▷ how to inform staff of a visitor's arrival – telephone, loudspeaker system, paging devices

▷ the importance of body language and what it means

▷ telephone system and operation

▷ how to use sources of information

▷ car parking arrangements for visitors to your organisation

▷ how to communicate effectively

What do you need to be able to do?

To achieve this you must be able to carry out the following over a specified period of time:

▷ greet visitors appropriately and identify their needs

▷ act in accordance with organisational policy

▷ take care not to disclose confidential information

▷ direct visitors or arrange for them to be escorted as required

▷ cope with delays or non-availability of staff politely

▷ keep the visitors' book up to date

▷ keep any other records up to date

▷ deal with emergencies in a calm and sensible manner

BACKGROUND KNOWLEDGE

As a receptionist you will need to know the structure, location and responsibilities of employees in your organisation. You will also need to know where people are located, their telephone extension numbers and the layout of your organisation. With this information, you will be well prepared for your job.

How to make this easy for yourself

Have a file which contains:

● an organisation chart
● a floor plan of the building(s) showing where offices are to be found
● an up-to-date list of internal telephone extensions
● an index system for recording regular callers

The receptionist is the first person a visitor sees.

How you should behave

● Smile, look pleasant, and *mean* it!
● Find out your visitor's name and use it.
● Make your visitors feel welcome.
● Pay attention to what is being said to you.
● If someone has to wait, offer him/her a seat/magazine/refreshments.
● Be polite, even with difficult people.

How you should look

● Neat and tidy
● Clean and well groomed (hair, hands etc.)
● Smartly dressed

How to use the appointments book

You will need to complete and check the appointments book every day. As soon as you receive details to be entered into the book, you should write them in neatly in the appropriate time slot. Make sure that you keep these appointments in the correct chronological order, and that you have all the information you require.

How to receive a visitor

Greet the visitor. Check the diary/appointments book to see if s/he is expected. Ask him/her to complete the visitor's book, and check that s/he is correctly parked if s/he has arrived by car. Inform the member of staff concerned that his/her visitor has arrived.

If the visitor has to wait, explain the delay and apologise, ask him/her to take a seat and offer magazines or newspapers. It is not often necessary for a receptionist to offer refreshments. Remember to be discreet and not to disclose any confidential information or to gossip.

How to direct visitors

As a receptionist must never leave the reception area unattended, you will need to direct visitors efficiently. This may mean using a floor plan, giving verbal directions, or arranging for an escort.

How to deal with messages

Receptionists may be asked to take messages over the telephone and from personal callers. These must be recorded accurately using the organisation's pre-printed form and passed on to the correct person as soon as possible.

How to deal with deliveries

All deliveries should arrive with a delivery note. You will need to check the following:

- Has it been delivered to the right place?
- Whom is it addressed to?
- How many packages are in the delivery? Are they all there?
- Is the delivery undamaged?

When you are satisfied with the above, you should sign for the package(s) and then contact the addressee to advise him/her that the order has arrived.

Suspicious packages

If there is no addressee, and no clear indication of the contents of the delivery, you should notify your superior immediately. Do not accept or sign for anything about which you are unsure. Do not attempt to open any such package.

Using the telephone system

All receptionists need a good telephone manner, and may be required to operate a switchboard which will require specialist training. Answer your telephone promptly using the appropriate greeting – for example, 'Reception, can I help you?'

Useful sources of information

Receptionists are often asked for information about travel, taxis, accommodation, road conditions, public transport, restaurants and directions. The reception desk should therefore have a wide range of reference material – maps, local directories, timetables, travel guides etc.

Dealing with people

Effective communication is necessary at all times in order to deal with all types of caller. It needs particular care with overseas visitors whose first language is not English, as well as with difficult or aggressive people.

Emergencies

If an accident should occur in the reception area, the receptionist needs to know basic first aid procedures. If necessary the emergency services should be called and someone in authority notified.

General notes

To gain competence in this unit, you will need to be observed receiving and directing visitors in your own workplace/training centre. You will need to greet visitors in the manner laid down by your company, and to follow all procedures required in respect of safety, security and emergencies.

You will need to demonstrate a thorough knowledge of your workplace/training centre, and to communicate effectively with colleagues by telephone, in writing and in face-to-face situations. You will need to be able to demonstrate that you can use reference books like street maps, handbooks etc. You must be able to explain why reception records are necessary.

You will be expected to demonstrate, in the workplace/training centre, all the areas listed above, and you will need to be observed carrying out these competences. It is expected that the demonstrations will be carried out over a period of time.

THE TASKS

Competence in receiving and directing visitors is best demonstrated in a real working situation over a period of time. The following role-play tasks will help you prepare for this.

Resources required by students/trainees

You will each require photocopies of the following:

▷ Tasks 13 and 14 – the page from the appointments book – two copies, one for 'today' and one for 'tomorrow'

Scenario

You are the receptionist at Leisurewear Ltd.

First, refer to the following general information, organisation chart and floor plan of the offices of Leisurewear Ltd. Then consider the situations outlined in the tasks and state the action you would take.

Leisurewear Limited – general information on the company

Leisurewear Ltd was set up by the Managing Director, Mr Paul Peterson, in 1975 in response to the growing demand for leisure clothing.

Mr Peterson began the company in a small office with only one other person to assist him – Mr Clive Clark, now Financial Director.

Mr Peterson and Mr Clark are determined that the company should expand, and are continually looking for ways to increase business. Staff are encouraged to put ideas forward at any time.

Today, the company has a thriving manufacturing section, its own transport fleet, a modern showroom and superb accommodation in the centre of Lichester.

All employees are offered a share of the profits after one year's employment, and are expected to show an interest in increasing productivity and in maintaining excellent standards.

Mr Peterson likes to get to know all employees, and operates a system of staff reviews every six months. Both he and Mrs Helen Clarke, the Personnel Director, take an interest in all staff progress and they offer, where possible, promotion from within the company.

The Sales Director, Mr Dennis Johnson, is an ex-athlete, and is very knowledgeable in the field of sportswear and leisurewear. Both he and the Showroom Manager, Mr George Baxter, travel frequently to Europe and the USA to find new lines. In the absence of Mr Johnson, Miss Tina Allen takes charge of the entire Sales programme.

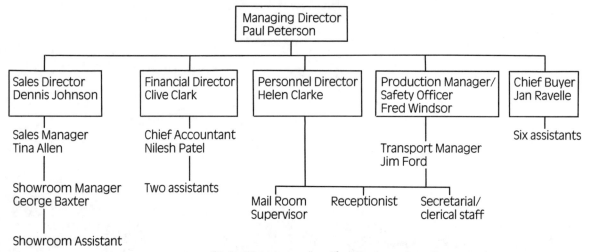

All directors have a seat on the board.
The chart shows lines of communications between staff, and who reports to whom.
The hierarchical level is not shown here.

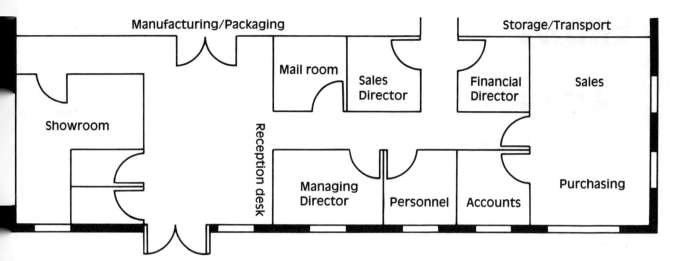

Floor plan of the offices of Leisurewear Limited

The Chief Buyer, Mrs Jan Ravelle, runs the Purchasing Department with a team of six staff. Mrs Ravelle joined the company in 1982 when she came to this country from France.

Mr Nilesh Patel, the Chief Accountant, offers support to Mr Clark, the Financial Director, and runs all the day-to-day accounting procedures in the company. He has two assistants.

The Production Department is run by Mr Fred Windsor, and the Transport Section by Mr Jim Ford. Mr Windsor is an electrical engineer and has responsibility for all the machines in the Manufacturing area. Mr Ford is responsible for the fleet of two lorries and four vans, as well as the cars used by senior members of staff. He is also responsible for the despatch of goods.

Mr Windsor is the current Safety Representative for the company.

TASK 1 Mrs Peterson arrives to see her husband urgently. You telephone Mr Peterson's secretary and are told he is in an important meeting and cannot be disturbed. What would you do?

TASK 2 A visitor arrives with a lunch appointment with Jan Ravelle. You know that Jan is off sick today. What would you do?

TASK 3 A sales representative arrives without an appointment and asks if you could do him a favour and get him in to see Jan Ravelle. You know that Jan normally does not see people without an appointment but he is very persistent. What would you do?

TASK 4 A college leaver arrives with an appointment to see Helen Clarke for an interview for the job of office junior. He is twenty minutes early and very nervous. What would you do?

TASK 5 Monsieur Artois arrives direct from the airport with his luggage. You are expecting him and know that he has a lunch appointment with Paul Peterson and Jan Ravelle. He asks if there is somewhere to freshen up and leave his luggage. What would you do?

TASK 6 A despatch rider arrives still wearing his helmet. You are totally unable to hear a word he says. He hands you a package and turns to leave. What would you do?

TASK 7

A young woman waiting for a job interview went into the cloakroom about half an hour ago. Her appointment is now overdue and she has not returned. What would you do?

TASK 8

You are asked to take a message for Nilesh Patel. His wife is at Heathrow awaiting the arrival of his mother-in-law on an international flight. The plane has been drastically delayed and they will have to spend the night at a hotel near the airport. They will therefore not be back for a planned family dinner tonight, and she is really worried about letting people know what has happened and about arrangements to collect a welcome home cake from Lichester Bakeries. What would you do?

TASK 9

Mr Peterson arrives at 10.00 a.m. furious to discover that a car is parked in his reserved space. He gives you the registration number and says 'Get it moved.' He asks you to write him a memo suggesting ways to avoid this happening again. What would you do?

TASK 10

A visitor, who has been to see Clive Clark, asks you to assist him. He wishes to know how to get to another appointment in Lichester. He then has to travel to London, and wishes to know the road conditions for later on today. He asks you whether you could advise him of two or three hotels where he might stay next time he is in the area. Which reference books will you use to help him? What would you do?

TASK 11

You have been busy dealing with several visitors, when you glance up and see a large brown package by the entrance. You are puzzled as it was not there before. You go and look at it – there is no marking on it at all. What would you do?

TASK 12

Señor Pancho Gonzales arrives from Spain to see Paul Peterson. He speaks very little English. You telephone Mr Peterson's secretary and she tells you that he is expected tomorrow, not today. What would you do?

TASK 13

As a receptionist, you will receive information from various members of staff to be entered into the appointments book. This information will vary from day to day. You may receive memos, notes or telephone calls advising you of the people expected to arrive.

   Enter the following telephone calls on to the appropriate pages of your appointments book.

(a) 'Hallo, Dennis Johnson's secretary here. Just to let you know that he is expecting three of our reps tomorrow at 10.00 a.m. They are: Peter Black, Janet Bailey and Sheena O'Donoghue.'

(b) 'Hi there, it's Jim from Transport here. I'm expecting a salesman from Renault tomorrow at about noon. I don't know his name, but he'll have his business card. Please ring me when he arrives and I'll come and collect him.'

(c) 'It's Tina Allen here. I'm lunching with a couple of our important customers tomorrow – Edward Myers and Jason Flitch of Metro Stores – and we are meeting here first for a quick look at our new range. They should be here at about 11.30. Please direct them to the showroom, and give me a ring to let me know when they have arrived.'

TASK 14

(a) Later on you receive the following four messages. Enter these on the appropriate pages of your appointments book.

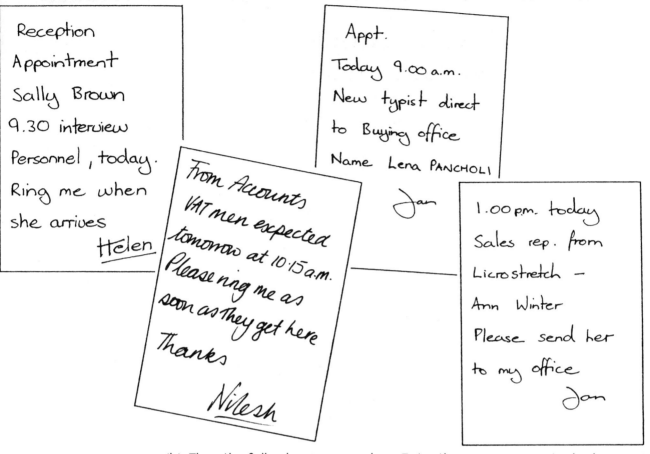

Reception
Appointment
Sally Brown
9.30 interview
Personnel, today.
Ring me when
she arrives
Helen

Appt.
Today 9.00 a.m.
New typist direct
to Buying office
Name Lena PANCHOLI
Jan

From Accounts
VAT men expected
tomorrow at 10.15 a.m.
Please ring me as
soon as they get here
Thanks
Nilesh

1.00 p.m. today
Sales rep. from
Licrostretch —
Ann Winter
Please send her
to my office
Jan

(b) Then the following memo arrives. Enter these arrangements also in your appointments book.

MEMO

From: Helen Clarke, Personnel
To: Receptionist

INTERVIEWS FOR POST OF SALES REPRESENTATIVE

Tomorrow, we are holding interviews for the above post. I am expecting the following candidates:

Thelma Boyce   10.00
Nina Cerrato   10.20
Michelle Cohen   10.40
George Court   11.00
Reg Kitching   11.20
Roy Mallipal   11.40

We shall be shortlisting from these six, and the second interviews will be in the afternoon. We will be providing a sandwich lunch in the Showroom at 12.00. Between interviews the candidates will wait in Reception. Please could you offer them coffee while they are waiting and order sandwiches and soft drinks from Silver Tray Catering for ten people. When the refreshments arrive, ring my secretary who will set up the lunch. Please also let her know when each candidate arrives.

After lunch we will advise the successful candidates and let you know the order for the second interviews.

ELEMENT 15.2   *Maintain reception area*

INTRODUCTION

What do you have to do?

▷ ensure that the reception area is always tidy and free from hazards

▷ keep displays and notices up to date and display them clearly

▷ make sure that all magazines and newspapers are always up to date

▷ have adequate stationery supplies

▷ make sure that all directories are up to date and available

▷ keep the reception area attended at all times

How well do you have to do it?

To achieve this you must be able to:

▷ make certain that the reception area is always clean and tidy

▷ deal with potential hazards – packages left lying around, slippery floors, uneven carpet etc.

▷ check daily that notices are up to date and that newspapers, magazines etc. are current and displayed neatly

▷ keep a stock check of essential supplies of stationery – message pads, memo paper, pens, pencils etc.

▷ make a daily check that all directories are available

▷ make sure that you have a stand-in receptionist available before you leave the area

What do you need to know?

▷ whom to contact if the reception area needs cleaning

▷ whom to contact if there are maintenance problems such as uneven carpet

▷ how supplies of reading material for the reception area are obtained

▷ how to display notices attractively

▷ how to operate a simple stock control system

▷ which directories should be available in reception

What do you need to be able to do?

To achieve this you must be able to carry out the following over a specified period of time:

▷ look after your reception area

▷ watch out for any potential hazards

▷ make the area welcoming and attractive for your visitors

▷ provide information as requested

▷ if you have to leave the reception area, remember to organise a stand-in

BACKGROUND KNOWLEDGE

Great care will have been given to the design of the reception area to make it easily accessible, welcoming, attractive and a pleasant working environment. Organisations often spend a considerable amount of money on this area as all visitors will see it. Sometimes, if a reception area is to be redesigned, the views of the receptionist will be sought.

As the person responsible for maintaining the reception area it is up to you to make sure that everything looks well organised and runs smoothly.

Remember that the reception area gives the first impression of your organisation to a visitor.

How to make this easy for yourself

- Have a daily routine and stick to it.
- Be observant.
- Check regularly that you have everything you need.
- Keep your records up to date – if you receive a new visitor's card, put it in your indexing system straight away. Remember to file it under the company name, not the individual's name.

Your responsibilities

As the receptionist you are not only responsible for keeping the area tidy, but also for the following:

Publicity material
Make sure this is always relevant and up to date. Go through it regularly sorting it out.

Displays and notices
Ensure that these are always looking fresh. No old or dog-eared notices should be left on the board. You should also see that they are attractively displayed and are easy to read.

Use your judgement to decide whether a notice is needed for cloakrooms, lifts, exits etc. If you have to prepare a notice, avoid handwritten ones unless it is an emergency. There are various commercial lettering sets available, or your organisation may have desktop publishing facilities.

Organisation charts
If one of these is displayed in your reception area, make sure that it is current. You should ensure that any additions/deletions are made as soon as possible and a new chart is drawn up to replace the out-of-date one.

Internal directories and stationery
Make sure that your internal directory is always current and available for reference. If you are also acting as telephonist, you will be required to provide an updated, accurate version for distribution to all members of staff.

You must make sure you always have adequate supplies of any stationery used in reception, such as telephone message pads, appointment cards (if appropriate), visitor's book and appointment book.

Health and safety
You will need to be aware of the implications of the Health and Safety at Work Act – your responsibility towards your own, your colleagues' and your visitors' safety while on the company premises. You should make sure that all equipment in the reception area is safe, including table lamps, standard lamps, portable heaters, fans, vending machines, payphones etc.

Effective liaison
As the receptionist you have an important liaison job – providing the links between visitors and your colleagues. You need to be able to liaise effectively at all levels.

You will deal with all members of the organisation and will need to develop a good working relationship with them. You should find out:

- whom you can contact direct by telephone – should you get through to his/her secretary first?
- who will see people without appointments
- who likes to collect their visitors, and who prefers them to be given directions

You will gradually get to know regular visitors to your company, and may be called upon to make conversation with them.

General notes

To gain competence in this unit, you will need to be observed working in and looking after a reception area to the standard required by your organisation.

You will be expected to demonstrate in the workplace all the elements listed above.

It is expected that the demonstrations will be carried out over a period of time.

THE TASKS

You will each require photocopies of the following:

▷ Task 5 – the stock requisition form – one copy

Scenario
You are the receptionist at Leisurewear, and are responsible for maintaining the reception area.

TASK 1

It is coming up to the time for your annual leave. A temporary replacement is to be employed to carry out your duties while you are on holiday. You are anxious that the reception area runs smoothly in your absence. Draw up:

(a) a daily maintenance routine which will help the 'temp' perform her/his duties. List the duties to be performed first thing in the morning, those that need to be carried out as the day progresses, and finally things which will need to be done at the end of the day.

(b) a list of hazards which could occur in a reception area and the steps to take to avoid them.

TASK 2

Occasionally floors become slippery in wet weather. There is no notice at present to warn visitors/staff of the possible hazard. Design a notice on A4 paper, bearing in mind that the lettering will be printed by desktop publishing.

TASK 3

You have been given a budget of £15 maximum to start a range of magazines which you think will be of interest to the customers who visit Leisurewear. Visit your local bookseller and research some titles. List them with the current price and indicate whether they are monthly or weekly publications.

TASK 4

The following members of staff have volunteered to cover the reception desk during your lunch breaks. You will need to draw up a rota for next month showing clearly who is on the desk, the date and time. Your lunch hour is usually 12 noon–1 p.m., but you can change it if necessary twice a week.
    The members of staff who have volunteered are:

Sue, a part-time member of staff who works on Mondays and Thursdays

Margaret, who is never available on a Wednesday

Carolyn, who is on annual leave for week three next month

Jonathan, who always lunches from 12 noon–1 p.m., so is not available then

    Try to distribute the cover evenly. Nobody should cover for two consecutive days.

TASK 5

You find that you have run out of the following:

Leisurewear colour brochures

telephone message pads

black ballpoint pens

    You should complete a stock requisition form for the above asking for 50 brochures, 6 message pads and 10 ballpoint pens.

TASK 6

You are not altogether happy with the telephone message pads you are provided with. Design an alternative which can be duplicated on A5 paper.

UNIT 16

ELEMENT 16.1 *Produce a variety of business documents from handwritten/typewritten drafts*

TEXT PROCESSING

INTRODUCTION

What do you have to do?

▷ type approximately 1200 words in a 2½-hour working period

▷ make sure all your work is of mailable standard

▷ follow 'house' style and typing conventions

▷ follow instructions for copies

How well do you have to do it?

To achieve this you must be able to:

▷ work at a speed of approximately 35 wpm

▷ correct all errors

▷ work within set deadlines

▷ follow spoken and written instructions

▷ plan your layout carefully, making the best use of paper

▷ spell and punctuate correctly

▷ deal with confidential material

What do you need to know?

▷ how to operate your machine correctly

▷ how to use a dictionary and other reference books

▷ the correct size of paper and envelopes to use for each task

▷ how to make corrections without spoiling the appearance of your work

▷ layout and display methods

▷ correct format for business correspondence

▷ how to take copies (carbon or photocopy)

▷ how to distribute copies

▷ how to file your copies

What do you need to be able to do?

▷ type from handwritten or typed copy

▷ follow all instructions carefully

▷ find information in one task to be used in another

▷ proof-read and correct work

▷ type the following range of documents and layouts: letters, memos, short reports, display, tabulation, completion of pre-printed forms, figure work

▷ rearrange material and make modifications to layout from drafts

▷ respond to any interruptions as necessary

BACKGROUND KNOWLEDGE

To demonstrate that you are competent you will have to complete three assignments which your tutor will give to you. You will need to discuss with your tutor when you are ready to undertake these assignments.

In the next section there are seven tasks – examples of the type of work you will be expected to do – which will give you practice before you attempt the assignments.

For the tasks, you are working in the Personnel Department of Leisurewear Ltd for Helen Clarke, the Personnel Director. Background information about the company and an organisation chart are given on pages 52–53.

THE TASKS

TASK 1

Please type the following report in single line spacing with at least a 2" (50mm) top margin. Please also make all corrections / amendments.

the past year

Summary of in-house training provided during ~~1989~~ CAPS please

u/c The personnel section has organised a wide variety of short in-house training courses for members of staff during ~~1989~~. These the past year ∧ fall mainly into two categories (a) specialised technical training and (b) management techniques.

Throughout the year as new clerical/secretarial staff joined the company they have attended a two day Familiarisation Course to enable them to operate our word processing system effectively. All new staff who have access to computers have attended two day a ∧ courses on Software Familiarisation.

ed
Our new sales and show room staff also attend a short ~~Familiarisation with the Product Course.~~ Product Induction Course.

In addition to the above we have held a number of management courses which have been delivered by outside providers, such as The Industrial Society. A list showing all courses and dates is will be ~~attached~~. The Section has carefully monitored the perceived circulated success of these courses by asking all staff to complete an later Assessment Report at the end of the course. Over 90% of these reports state satisfaction with the course and achievement of the stated objectives.

Conference There is one innovation planned for the current year and that is a Residential Sales ~~Course~~ lasting three days to be held in a hotel. In addition to the serious work content of the conference it is planned to include a presentation dinner at which our CAPS Salesperson Of The Year will receive his/her cheque. Firm estimates for the cost of this venture are still being sought.

A report to the Managing Director following a recent training course

TASK 2

> Please could you type a memo to accompany this Report to the M.D.
> Tell him a list of all courses referred to will be ready by next Wednesday (please insert date)
> Thanks Helen.

Composition of a memo to accompany Task 1

TASK 3

> Please type this on Leisurewear Ltd official memo paper. Make all amendments as shown. Date it for today.

MEMORANDUM

To: All Staff

From: Helen Clark / Personnel ~~Officer~~ *Director*

e /

VISUAL DISPLAY UNITS - HEALTH AND SAFETY

The following has been agreed between Management and staff representatives regarding all employees using VDU equipment. *during working hours*

All employees will be encouraged to have their eyes tested /by a qualified optician *of their own choosing* before starting work using any VDU equipment. The tests should be repeated regularly and / *a copy of* the results made available to the employer.

The firm will provide a letter for the employee to give to the optician indicating that the eyesight tests should be to the standards laid down for VDU operators by the Association of Optical Practitioners.

Where the need for an employee to wear spectacles to operate a VDU has been established by reference to an optician, the firm will make a contribution to the cost. / *up to a maximum of £100*

Where a VDU operator who is pregnant is anxious about using the equipment, arrangements will be made / to find alternative work, *setting out the working conditions and* without financial or conditions of employment detriment. After maternity leave, she will be expected to return to her original duties. *at her request*

or distress

If a person reports any discomfort / when using a VDU, the management will make every effort to investigate the cause.

Staff should report such problems to their immediate supervisor who will inform the Personnel Director.

A memo for staff regarding VDUs

TASK 4

Mr Alan Johnson
10 Water Lane
LICHESTER
L16 4BJ

(please take one copy and type an envelope)

Dear Mr Johnson

Showroom Assistant   ← *Caps and underscore please*

Thank you for your completed application form in respect of the above position at our Lichester showroom

Would you please ~~attend~~ *come along* for interview on Thursday ✓ 17 February at 2 pm, reporting to Reception on your arrival. Should this time not be convenient, please contact my secretary *on extension 14* to arrange another date. You will be seen by Mr George Baxter, our Showroom Manager, and myself. Kindly bring any examination certificates *mentioned in your application* with you. I look forward to meeting you on 17 February.

Yours sincerely
LEISUREWEAR LTD

Helen Clarke
Personnel Director

A letter inviting someone for interview with envelope and copy

TASK 5

Miss Caroline Peters
Flat 7
42 Beecholme
LICHESTER
LI2 3SR

BEECHOLME

Take one copy and type an envelope please

Mark it confidential

Dear Miss Peters

RECEPTIONIST

Thank you for attending an interview for the post of Receptionist with us. I am delighted to be able to offer you the position, subject to satisfactory references and a medical report. Please confirm your acceptance, as soon as possible.

, in writing,

Your starting salary is shown on the enclosed scale and rises £750 per annum on satisfactory completion of a 3-month probationary period. Holiday entitlement is 4 weeks plus all public holidays. This rises ~~goes up~~ ✓ to 5 weeks after 2 years with the company.

I understand your College course is nearing its end but that you do have examination commitments. Please telephone me next week to discuss possible start dates. Will you also let me know if you have made any holiday arrangements — Leisurewear will honour these of course.

for this year

Yours s_____
L_____ LTD

H_____ C _____
Personnel D _____

A confidential letter offering a job

TASK 6

Typist - please complete the heading with today's date
Please calculate the number of years and months of
service for each member of staff and enter this information
in the final columns.

Take an extra copy for reproducing and sending to each
member of staff. Do not make more than <u>one</u> copy unless
you are instructed to do so.

LENGTH OF SERVICE OF PERSONNEL DATED				199-
NAME	POSITION	DATE JOINED	LENGTH OF SERVICE YEARS	MONTHS
Paul Peterson	Managing Director	Aug 1975		
Dennis Johnson	Sales Director	Jan 1987		
Clive Clark	Financial Director	Aug 1975		
Helen Clarke	Personnel Director	Sept 1989		
Fred Windsor	Production Manager	Jan 1985		
Jan Ravelle	Chief Buyer	July 1982		
Tina Allen	Sales Manager	May 1988		
Nilesh Patel	Chief Accountant	Oct 1986		
Jim Ford	Transport Manager	Dec 1977		
George Baxter	Showroom Manager	Mar 1984		

A table showing length of service of key personnel

TASK 7

You can get a copy of the form to complete from your tutor.

Please fill in the form for the
WILCHESTER MANAGEMENT CENTRE
with your own details
I'd like you to go on this course.
Choose the dates you'd prefer.
The company will pay for you. Helen

UNIT 17

ELEMENT 17.1 *Produce a variety of business documents from recorded speech*

AUDIO TRANSCRIPTION

INTRODUCTION

What do you have to do?

▷ type a variety of business documents of approximately 600 words from recorded speech, following recorded instructions, within 1½ hours

▷ check through your work to make sure it is correct

▷ correct any errors

▷ lay out work according to acceptable standards or 'house' style

▷ follow instructions for copies

▷ operate your equipment correctly and safely at all times

How well do you have to do it?

To achieve this you must be able to:

▷ interpret oral instructions correctly

▷ estimate the size of paper to use

▷ plan your layout carefully, making the best use of the paper

▷ listen to groups of words, remember them and type them

▷ correct all errors

▷ spell and punctuate correctly

▷ use a dictionary

▷ deal with confidential information

What do you need to know?

▷ how to operate your audio equipment

▷ how to operate your typewriter

▷ English grammar

▷ business terms

▷ paper sizes – how much text fits on a sheet with at least 1" margins all round

▷ accepted typing styles

What do you need to be able to do?

▷ audio-type a range of material, including letters, memos, short reports, and messages

▷ complete the given work within 1½ hours

BACKGROUND KNOWLEDGE

To demonstrate competence in this unit you should be a competent keyboard operator (the keyboard may be a typewriter or a wordprocessor). You should have a sound knowledge of typewriting rules and display methods, including letters, memos, simple tables, short reports and notices.

Good working habits

Make sure that your audio equipment is safely positioned on your desk, and that there are no trailing wires.

Always zero the tape counter (if there is one) before you start audio-typing.

Make a note of the counter number where each piece of work starts in order to rewind it for checking.

Listen carefully to instructions regarding carbon copies, special marks, envelopes, etc.

Use your dictionary to check awkward spellings, or any that you are unsure of.

If you cannot understand a word, carry on listening without typing, to see if this helps you. If there is previous correspondence, check whether this helps you.

Remember – what you type *must* make sense.

To check your work: rewind your tape to the beginning of the task, leave your paper in the typewriter, and read what you have typed as you listen.

Correct any errors you may find as you go along.

Rewind the tape fully when you have finished your work.

Keep a tidy desk at all times.

THE TASKS

You will need to discuss with your tutor when you are ready to undertake the tasks and assignments in this unit. Your readiness to attempt them will depend on your keyboarding ability. To demonstrate that you are competent, you will have to complete all three of the assignments that your tutor will give you after you have completed the tasks.

Resources required by students/trainees

You will each require the following:

▷ A copy of a cassette with Tasks 1, 2, 3 and 4 recorded on it

Scenario

You are working for Nilesh Patel, Chief Accountant of Leisurewear Limited. He has left you a cassette on which there are the following four pieces of work for you to transcribe:

Task 1 – memo to all sales staff re travel claims
Task 2 – notice for staff noticeboard re petty cash
Task 3 – notice of staff sale
Task 4 – letter to Newphone Limited

Deal with all four tasks and date for today.

UNIT 18

ELEMENT 18.1 *Produce a variety of business documents from dictated material*

INTRODUCTION

What do you have to do?

▷ take dictation notes of 375–400 words at a minimum of 70 wpm

▷ check through your notes to make sure they are correct

▷ produce typed or wordprocessed scripts from your notes

▷ make sure your work is correct and of mailable standard

▷ follow instructions for copies

▷ check any uncertainties in text with the dictator

How well do you have to do it?

To achieve this you must be able to:

▷ take shorthand at approximately 70 wpm

▷ be able to read back your notes correctly

▷ type or wordprocess accurate material from your notes

▷ correct all errors

▷ spell and punctuate correctly

▷ deal with confidential material

▷ follow spoken and written instructions

▷ plan your layout carefully, making the best use of the paper

What do you need to know?

▷ one shorthand system in detail

▷ business terms

▷ English grammar

▷ accepted typing styles

What do you need to be able to do?

▷ take down in shorthand a range of dictated material including letters, memos and short reports

▷ write shorthand for up to 6 minutes at 70 wpm

▷ transcribe from your notes within one hour

BACKGROUND KNOWLEDGE

You may be given material for typing or wordprocessing in various forms. It may be handwritten, typed or dictated. It is essential to produce all typewritten or wordprocessed work to the same high standard. All the usual typing rules will apply when you are typing or wordprocessing from your shorthand notes.

Good working habits

Remember to date your shorthand notes at the foot of the page.

Use a margin in your shorthand notebook for amendments or corrections.

Listen carefully for instructions regarding carbon copies, special marks, envelopes etc.

Have a spare pen/pencil ready.

Remember to indicate when you have completed a piece of transcription by ticking or crossing through.

Use your dictionary to help with difficult spellings.

Keep a tidy desk.

THE TASKS

For all shorthand transcription material you are working for Dennis Johnson, Sales Director of Leisurewear Limited. You are also expected to work for Tina Allen, the Sales Manager. The two warm-up tasks are set in Tina Allen's office. One will be a response to the following letter from Lichester Boys' Football Club, and the other will be a memo.

You have been called in for dictation today.

LICHESTER BOYS' FOOTBALL CLUB

Secretary

John Booth
26a High Street Green
LICHESTER

Tel. 44560

The Managing Director
Leisurewear Limited
Lion House
LICHESTER
L12 7PR

4 April 199—

Dear Sir

I am writing on behalf of the Lichester Boys' Football Club, which as you may know has just won the local league cup. The Club has been in existence for two years and we now have five teams of boys playing regularly. Of course all boys pay a membership subscription, which goes towards the cost of hiring grounds and getting our teams to away matches. However, this fee will not cover the cost of club kit for our players and we would like to provide our first team with a suitable strip. I have been asked by the Club Committee to approach you to see if Leisurewear Limited would be willing to support the club by providing two sets of first team strip.

In addition to this possible financial or material help, we are inviting important local business people to come to our next major fixture as our guests. We are seeking the active support of local companies and organisations. It therefore gives me great pleasure to invite you to join us at Cavendish School on Saturday next at 11.00 a.m. when we shall be playing in an important local Derby. Light refreshments will be served after the game in the school hall.

I look forward to hearing whether you can join us on this special occasion and also whether you feel your organisation could help us in the very practical way described above.

Yours faithfully

John Booth
Honorary Secretary
Lichester Boys' Football Club

Letter from Lichester Boys' Football Club for reply

UNIT 19

ELEMENT 19.1 *Make travel arrangements and book accommodation*

ARRANGING TRAVEL AND MEETINGS

INTRODUCTION

What do you have to do?

▷ make enquiries and obtain necessary information

▷ organise arrangements using booking procedures and the organisation's allowance structures

▷ make travel arrangements, using maps, timetables, and directories

▷ make hotel reservations, using hotel guides

▷ use travel agencies, if appropriate

▷ apply national and international telephone procedures

▷ estimate costs

▷ use a calculator for British and foreign currency conversion

▷ obtain currency and/or travellers cheques, if appropriate

▷ write letters of confirmation

▷ record details of arrangements

▷ deal with common travel constraints such as delays and surcharges

How well do you have to do it?

To achieve this you must be able to:

▷ gather the appropriate information together

▷ follow organisation rules

▷ carry out instructions

▷ meet deadlines

▷ deal with customers and clients

▷ find the necessary information for organising travel, hotel reservations, currency, travellers cheques, visas and vaccinations if necessary

▷ produce mailable letters of confirmation which are error free

▷ record information accurately

▷ meet deadlines for producing details of arrangements and the necessary documents

What do you need to know?

▷ the policy of the organisation regarding booking procedures and allowance structures

▷ how to carry out instructions and organise arrangements

▷ the necessary travel documentation (passports, travellers cheques, foreign currency)

▷ how to estimate costs using a calculator

▷ where to obtain relevant travel information and finance (timetables, directories, hotel guides, maps, agencies)

▷ the importance of exchange rates and British and foreign currency conversion for financing foreign travel

▷ how to compose a confirmation letter

▷ national and international telephone procedures

▷ common travel constraints such as delays and surcharges

What do you need to be able to do?

▷ carry out instructions and make arrangements according to organisation policy

▷ collate information

▷ make and record appointments

▷ make travel arrangements at home and abroad, by road, rail and air

▷ use timetables, directories, hotel guides and maps

▷ make hotel reservations

▷ obtain currency and travellers cheques

▷ fill out necessary forms for travel

▷ make arrangements regarding car hire

▷ estimate costs and produce final costs

▷ complete diary pages

▷ write letters of confirmation

▷ produce accurate written details of arrangements and distribute them to participants

▷ use a travel computer package or Prestel

BACKGROUND KNOWLEDGE

In business, managers and their staff are more and more frequently involved in organising business trips in the UK and abroad. This could be to meet business associates or customers, to promote sales, or to attend exhibitions, trade fairs and conferences.

Organising travel

It is the duty of the person organising a visit to make sure it is successful. You must make sure the people travelling arrive in time and have the correct paperwork, and that the journey and accommodation are as trouble free as possible.

In order to do this you must discuss the trip with the people travelling, and make all the necessary enquiries and reservations for air, rail, sea or motor travel and hotel accommodation. Ensure that you prepare an itinerary and additional information, and have the necessary travel documents available. Double check all departure and arrival times.

You must make sure the arrangements are completely reliable and check every detail carefully. Keep the itinerary simple and not too overcrowded – you need to allow time for rest. Anticipate things that may be needed and things likely to go wrong. Check out alternative travel arrangements in case of delays, strikes or bad weather.

Make sure you organise things like vaccinations or visas and provide all the necessary documents well in advance. Fax and telephone can be very helpful, but don't rely on them for last-minute arrangements. Bookings should be confirmed in writing, well in advance of travel.

Telephone calls

When making national telephone calls, remember to check the telephone number you are dialling, and look up the correct national code for long distance calls in the British Telecom code book. Try to phone when the charges are cheaper – this information is in your local telephone book.

If you are dialling abroad, remember all countries have their own international code, usually followed by an area code, and then the number you are calling. The British Telecom code book will give you this information. Again, look in your local phone book to see the cheapest time to phone. Sometimes the ringing and engaged tones abroad are different from those in the UK. If in doubt, telephone the British Telecom international operator on 155.

Books and guides

For travelling by rail, the *British Rail ABC Guide* or *Intercity Guide* to services is a very useful reference book. Many facilities can be reserved in advance.

For air travel, tickets are available from local travel agents, and airline desks. Parking at airports can be booked in advance. Make sure you book scheduled flights as they are more reliable than stand-by or cheap flights.

Cromer's Office Companion is a very useful reference book, which contains a wealth of information on travel requirements for different countries. It is loose-leaf and can be updated every year. There are useful guides to British Hotels produced by the AA and RAC, which show the facilities and prices.

Booking hotels

Most hotels will accept telephone bookings, but confirmation should be made in writing, by letter, fax or telex. Make sure you write down the essential points of the booking before telephoning the hotel. Check the tariff, method of payment, car parking arrangements, room facilities and restaurant details.

Travelling abroad

For travelling abroad, travel agencies offer a wide service including reservations for travel and hotel, car hire, insurance, travellers cheques and foreign currency. They can also advise on necessary visas and vaccinations, and recommended medical supplies.

Travellers cheques and foreign currency can also be obtained from banks. It is important to be aware of the exchange rate for the country being visited as this will affect finance.

Obviously check that travellers have current passports, and Green Card insurance if they are driving abroad. An international driving licence is requested in some countries. In most countries you need to be at least 21 to hire a car, so check the rules carefully.

Travelling by car

If you are taking a British car to Europe, sit down with a route planning map of Europe, and remember that quite expensive tolls are charged on motorways in most European countries.

If you are travelling to an Eastern European country, check with the relevant embassies or tourist authorities before you go. Many personal insurance policies do not cover Eastern Europe. Crossing borders may take time and finding high grade petrol can be difficult. Most East European countries require you to buy coupons on the border and pay in Western currency.

Many countries have a zero drink-drive limit and you could face licence confiscation or imprisonment if caught with alcohol in your blood. Remember different countries have different speed limits, and dipped headlights are needed at night in most countries. RAC Eurocover Motoring Assistance and AA 5-Star Service offer full breakdown protection abroad. However, make sure you have your car serviced before you take it abroad.

The documents you must have when taking your car abroad are passports, ferry tickets, driving licence, original vehicle registration document, insurance certificate, Green Card, a GB sign, headlamp adjusters for night driving (and yellow colouring for France), travellers cheques and money. Also some countries insist on a set of spare bulbs, first aid kit, spare spectacles or contact lenses, if worn, fire extinguisher, outside mirrors on both sides, and an international driving licence from the AA or RAC.

It would also be advisable to take a map book or route map, guide books, hotel and restaurant guides, breakdown cover and travel insurance, a few tools, a kit of spare parts for the car, and fuel coupons for Italy and some East European countries.

Form E111 for free medical treatment in EC countries is available from the Department of Health. Do not forget Prestel and viewdata for information and booking services.

You will need money for travel, accommodation and meals not paid for in advance.

Money

Cash
Some cash is essential. You need sterling to cover journeys in Britain and/or at the airport and also an extra sum to change abroad in case of emergency. Also take foreign currency to tide you over on arrival.

Travellers cheques
These can be bought in Britain, from banks, building societies or travel agents, and you can exchange them for cash or pay bills with them abroad. In sterling they usually range from £10 to £100. The larger ones should be cashed first.

It is not usually beneficial to buy travellers cheques in foreign currencies. It can be useful, though, to have travellers cheques in American dollars if you are going to the USA, where they are widely accepted instead of cash.

Eurocheques
These can be bought from the bank with two weeks' notice. They usually come in books of ten with a cheque card to guarantee them. They are valid in about forty countries.

Eurocheques can be written in local currency and the equivalent in sterling is taken out of your bank account in Great Britain. They are not cheap but they are a good standby.

Postcheques
With a Girobank current account and cheque card you can buy postcheques, valid in over thirty countries. They can be used to draw a sum up to the local equivalent of £120 without charge. They cannot be used in shops or hotels.

Credit cards
Visa credit cards and Eurocards can be used in most countries. You can draw local currency up to the equivalent of £100 a day and use cash dispensers with your PIN number. In some countries they are not widely accepted for petrol, and large bills may need time for clearance.

For travelling in Britain you will probably need cash, credit cards, cheque book and cheque card.

THE TASKS

Resources required by students/trainees

You will each require photocopies of the following:

▷ Tasks 1 and 6 – the blank memo form – two copies

▷ Task 5 – the blank sales invoice – one copy

You will need to obtain the following:

▷ Task 6 – a brochure from a travel agent for a ferry company from Dover to Ostend; a map of Europe and a national newspaper for current exchange rates

TASK 1

You work for Young Wares plc, 18 Green Street, Hertford, Herts SG13 8EF, telephone 0992 75361. Your company is organising a Sales Conference for two days at the Bell Tower Hotel, Greaves Street, Blackpool, Lancs FY4 3RL, telephone 0253 68461, on 22 and 23 May. This is to discuss the expansion of the export side of the business. In particular, it is hoped to export jeans to Eastern Europe.

Write a memo from the Sales Manager's Secretary to be distributed to all sales staff and representatives, asking them to attend this important conference. If staff have other commitments they should let the Secretary know as soon as possible.

TASK 2

Some preliminary enquiries have been made about accommodation at the Bell Tower Hotel. Telephone the hotel and make a booking for twenty-two members of your company for the three nights of 21, 22 and 23 May. This should be for twelve single and five twin rooms, half board, to include breakfast and dinner. Some members of staff have agreed to share because of the shortage of single rooms available.

Book a suite of two rooms for the meetings, each room to hold thirty people. An overhead projector and a TV/video will be needed for both days. Morning coffee and a buffet lunch is to be laid on in the suite.

Confirm by letter.

TASK 3

Compile a programme for the two days from 10 a.m. to 5 p.m. It should include the events below.

Day 1 – 22 May
The conference will start with an introduction by the Sales Manager. There will then be a half-hour video on the Eastern European sales promotion, followed by a thirty-minute talk from Mr W. Jenkins, the designer of the new jeans and denim clothes. You should allow time for a question and answer session.

Lunch will be in the restaurant between 1 p.m. and 2 p.m. After lunch, there will be a two-hour fashion show of new products in denim.

Day 2 – 23 May
The second day will start with an hour-long talk by the Sales Director about selling techniques abroad, followed by a two-hour practical workshop on selling techniques.

Lunch will be in the restaurant between 12 noon and 1 p.m. After lunch, the Export Manager will talk for two hours on the regulations and paperwork involved in export. There will then be a two-hour practical workshop on export paperwork, followed at 5 p.m. by a short closing speech from the Sales Manager.

TASK 4

You have received the following fax from a company representative, Mr W. Browning, 29 North Street, Folkestone, Kent, fax number 0303 38421.

The fax from Mr Browning

```
I am travelling from London Euston to
Blackpool by train.
Would you be kind enough to look up the
times of two trains after 12 noon on 21
May. I need times of departure from Euston
and arrival at Blackpool.
Also the times of two trains after 9 a.m.
on 24 May, going from Blackpool to Euston.
Could you please find out the cost of 1st
and 2nd class travel.
```

Send a fax back to the representative giving him this information.

TASK 5

Complete an invoice from the hotel, no. 56891 dated 3 June, showing the following details and total cost of the conference:

1 suite hire £70 per day + VAT
1 overhead projector £20 per day + VAT
1 TV/video £25 per day + VAT
44 morning coffees 50p each + VAT
44 buffet lunches £3.30 each + VAT
44 dinners £9.50 each + VAT
5 twin doubles with breakfast and dinner £65 per person per night + VAT
12 single rooms with breakfast and dinner £82 per person per night + VAT
Invoice total

TASK 6

You work for Young Wares plc, 18 Green Street, Hertford, Herts SG13 8EF, telephone 0992 75361. One of your salesmen, Mr R. North, has been invited to Brussels on 8, 9 and 10 June, to quote for supplying new uniforms for the staff of a large retail company.

(a) Contact your local travel agency and obtain a brochure from a ferry company for Dover to Ostend. The salesman wishes to take his car abroad with him and is staying three days.

(b) Fill in the booking form for the ferry. Hotel accommodation is being arranged by the company in Brussels at The Mecca Hotel, Lindenstrasse 221, Brussels.

(c) Produce an itinerary for Mr North's travel arrangements.

(d) Trace his road route from a map of Europe.

(e) Mr North wishes to take £250 in Belgian currency. Using the current exchange rate guide in a national newspaper, calculate how many Belgian francs he will get for his pounds.

(f) Find out from your local bank how much commission they charge for obtaining currency. Deduct the commission the bank will charge and state the number of Belgian francs obtained for your £250.

(g) Compose a memo to Mr North enclosing the itinerary and map. List the documents and equipment he will need for his journey. Also advise him of the advantages of taking cash, travellers cheques, Eurocheques and credit cards abroad.

ELEMENT 19.2 *Arrange meetings involving three or more people*

INTRODUCTION

What do you have to do?

▷ identify requirements and calculate costs

▷ contact the people involved

▷ make sure they are available

▷ use information sources such as timetables, directories, reference books and hotel guides

▷ book a place of meeting using the organisation's procedures

▷ book required equipment using local suppliers if necessary

▷ order refreshments using local caterers

▷ arrange car parking

▷ prepare meeting papers

▷ confirm details of a meeting by letter and telephone

▷ issue papers to people attending

▷ check the meeting room is prepared

How well do you have to do it?

To achieve this you must be able to:

▷ gather in information accurately

▷ find out personnel requirements

▷ receive and pass on information, verbally and in writing

▷ pass on clear and accurate messages

▷ prepare meeting papers in good time

▷ confirm details accurately and to a mailable standard

▷ issue papers according to instructions

▷ prepare the meeting room in advance

▷ deal with unexpected things that occur

What do you need to know?

▷ how to communicate well orally and in writing

▷ how to calculate costs and requirements for meetings

▷ the structure and location of the organisation and the responsibilities of staff

▷ local suppliers and services in your area such as caterers, car parking and visual aid hire

▷ how to use information sources such as timetables, directories, reference books and hotel guides

▷ how to make a detailed telephone call

▷ the type of meeting, protocol and documentation needed

What do you need to be able to do?

▷ contact people attending the meeting

▷ communicate with colleagues

▷ use directories, reference books, timetables and hotel guides for information

▷ make telephone calls

▷ book a meeting room, with necessary equipment

▷ order refreshments/lunch

▷ make car parking arrangements

▷ prepare meeting papers

▷ complete diary entries

▷ confirm details by letter and telephone

▷ issue meeting papers to people attending

▷ check the meeting room

BACKGROUND KNOWLEDGE

More and more time in business is spent in meetings, so their cost in time is very high. Therefore it is essential that they are organised properly so that they are effective.

You should first identify the purpose of the meeting and make the necessary arrangements. Meetings are held for a variety of purposes: to discuss important matters, solve problems, negotiate agreements, plan policies and strategies, investigate progress and report back, brief staff, stimulate new ideas and interview staff.

Meetings can be formal or informal. Formal meetings have a chairperson, follow procedures and have paperwork in the form of agenda and minutes. Informal meetings usually include a leader but no laid-down procedure and may be a working party, training or problem solving group, or a brainstorming session.

Some meetings are held by tele-conferencing in local studios. TV cameras and audio equipment are used to link each group of people in the separate studios.

Organising meetings

If you are organising a meeting, make sure that all the people attending are available by contacting them. Entries should be made in their diaries. You may have to offer alternative dates and times. Some regular meetings have a fixed date and time.

It is important to decide the most convenient place to hold the meeting. Some meetings may be held in a regular meeting room. You should choose a quiet environment, and make sure there are no interruptions.

You will need to arrange refreshments, perhaps with outside caterers, and check car parking facilities. Any necessary equipment, such as overhead projectors and video recorders, should be organised.

Paperwork for formal meetings

The paperwork for a formal meeting is very important. You must first notify the people who are attending. The necessary details are: title of meeting, place, date, time and person calling the meeting. This **notice of meeting** could be an advertisement in the local paper, a leaflet, a notice or a memo. It is usual to give 7–14 days' notice.

The **agenda** is then prepared. This is a list of items to be dealt with at the meeting. Some standard items are:

apologies for absence

minutes of last meeting

matters arising from the last meeting

reports

any other business

the date of the next meeting

Sometimes a chairperson's agenda is prepared with extra information and space for notes to be written.

You may be required to ask someone to take the **minutes** (the record of what happens). These are typed up afterwards and circulated to all the people who attended.

Arrangements in advance and on the day

If you are organising a meeting, you should do the following things in advance:

contact participants

make a note in diaries

book a room if necessary

organise refreshments and equipment

reserve parking spaces

prepare and send out a notice of the meeting, an agenda and any other necessary documents

prepare place names if needed

You should do the following things on the day:

check the room – furniture arrangements, lighting, temperature, ventilation, water and glasses, place names, writing materials and ashtrays

lay out documents

check equipment

confirm refreshments

instruct the switchboard to transfer calls if it is an in-house meeting

inform reception

check car parking

have diaries available

receive members attending

place a meeting notice on the door so it is not disturbed

THE TASKS

Resources required by students/trainees

You will each require photocopies of the following:

▷ Task 3 – the fire evacuation notice – one copy

▷ Task 5 – the order form – one copy

TASK 1

You work for Young Wares plc, 18 Green Street, Hertford, Herts SG13 8EF, telephone 0992 75361.

Your Managing Director has asked you to arrange a meeting for five managers to discuss safety and security at your firm. The Chief Inspector from the local police will also attend.

There has recently been a break-in, and valuable equipment – calculators, two computers and stationery – has been stolen from the Accounts Department. The company has also been plagued with hoax bomb threat calls recently.

(a) This meeting will be held on 9 May at 2 p.m. As the board room is being redecorated it is to be held outside the firm. Use the hotel guide to choose a suitable local hotel.

(b) Send a letter of enquiry to the hotel for booking a suitable private room for the meeting. A buffet lunch will be required and you will need to have a video and an overhead projector and screen. Also ask about the car parking facilities for the seven people attending.

TASK 2

Prepare an agenda for this meeting. Subjects to be discussed are:

• security (recent break-in on 28 April)
• reordering of new equipment
• claim for equipment from the insurance company
• visit of the insurance company to advise on security
• need for security of personnel records on the new computer system
• procedure for evacuation in case of fire/bomb threats
• review of fire-fighting equipment
• appointment of a fire officer
• any other business

TASK 3

Compose a notice of the meeting. Lunch will be provided 1–2 p.m. Attach to the notice the agenda prepared in Task 2, and the fire evacuation notice provided.

TASK 4

There is to be a follow-up meeting on 16 May. This will be in the board room as the decorating has been completed. However, you will need an outside caterer to provide the lunch.

Look in your local Yellow Pages telephone directory and choose a caterer. Make a telephone enquiry for the price of lunch for seven people in a private room. You require a cold buffet.

TASK 5

Place an order with the caterer, using the order form provided, for seven lunches for the meeting on 16 May in the board room. The order number is 8045815, dated 2 May 199–.

ELEMENT 20.1 *Make and record petty cash payments*

PROCESSING PAYMENTS

INTRODUCTION

What do you have to do?

▷ make and record petty cash transactions

How well do you have to do it?

To achieve this you must be able to:

▷ record accurately all transactions and provide authorised petty cash vouchers

▷ record accurately cash withdrawals from the main cash account

▷ investigate all queries and take prompt action

▷ balance petty cash book records and keep an accurate account of cash

▷ follow confidentiality procedures

What do you need to know?

▷ how to operate a petty cash system including recording procedures and authorisations

▷ how to be responsible for handling the day-to-day petty cash transactions using an imprest system

▷ how to use appropriate headings for expenditures

What do you need to be able to do?

▷ process petty cash transactions for at least one month

▷ support these transactions with copies of records, vouchers and receipts

BACKGROUND KNOWLEDGE

In double-entry book-keeping the record of each business account is divided into two parts. The left-hand side, called **debit**, records value received; the right-hand side, called **credit**, records the amount of cash paid.

Details of cash transactions are usually kept in the cash book. The cash book records money received by the business (**income**), and money paid out (**expenditure**). Some businesses record both income and expenditure in one book, others use a separate book for each. Whichever system is used the cash book is totalled at the end of each period (usually one month).

Small payments within the company are generally not put through the main cash book. Instead the cashier will credit the cash book with a sum of money allocated to petty cash and the petty cashier will debit this amount, called the **float** or **imprest**, in the petty cash book.

Payments made from petty cash are entered on the credit side of the petty cash book in analysis columns, such as 'Travel' and 'Stationery', which show immediately how much is spent on different items. VAT is always shown in a separate column because it can be reclaimed from Customs and Excise. Payments from petty cash must always be supported by vouchers or receipts.

Payments can be made from petty cash until the float is used up, when the cashier will replace the initial amount of money. However, most companies choose to use the imprest system for recording petty cash, whereby payments are entered on the credit side and the book is balanced at pre-determined intervals, usually weekly or monthly. The petty cash book is then taken to the cashier, who will reimburse the petty cashier with an amount equal to the value of the vouchers or receipts. This will restore the imprest to the original amount. For example:

1 January	The cashier gives the petty cashier	£100.00
	The petty cashier pays out during January	£ 97.95
	Petty cash in hand	£ 2.05
	Cashier restores imprest by reimbursing the amount spent	£ 97.95
1 February	Petty cash in hand	£100.00

Petty cash vouchers will be numbered consecutively by the petty cashier and entered into the correct columns of the petty cash book.

The amount of cash in hand, plus the total value of the vouchers, should always equal the original float. To complete the double entry, the total of each expense column is entered in the relevant analysis columns in the cash book before being debited to the relevant expense account in the general ledger.

Petty cash vouchers and receipts should be filed securely. The petty cash money should always be kept in a locked cash box and placed in a locked drawer, cabinet or safe to which only the person responsible has the key.

THE TASK

Before proceeding with this unit you should *either* complete all the Level I tasks in Unit 4, Element 4.1 *Process petty cash transactions, or* provide evidence that you can meet the performance criteria required for that element.

Resources required by students/trainees

You will each require photocopies of the following:

▷ Page 21 of the petty cash book – one copy

▷ Cash book expenditure page for February 199– – one copy

You will also require:

▷ A calculator

You have balanced page 21 of the petty cash book (provided) and are required to restore the imprest on 1 February.

(a) Enter the correct amounts in the relevant analysis columns in the cash book. Use the page headed 'Expenditure' and dated February 199– (provided).

(b) On this page of the cash book, enter the total amount paid out to petty cash on 1 February.

(c) Enter the amount received from the cashier on page 21 of the petty cash book for 2 February.

ELEMENT 20.2   *Receive and record payments and issue receipts*

INTRODUCTION

What do you have to do?

▷ count cash correctly and give change correctly where applicable

▷ verify cheque and credit card payments correctly prior to acceptance

▷ complete and issue all receipts correctly

▷ identify and deal with all discrepancies in accordance with laid-down procedures

▷ follow security procedures at all times

▷ keep records up to date, legibly and accurately

How well do you have to do it?

To achieve this you must be able to:

▷ identify and take action on out-of-date credit or cheque validation cards

▷ ensure customers do not overspend credit limits

▷ deal with incorrect or incomplete cheques

▷ count cash correctly

▷ give correct change when necessary

▷ communicate effectively

What do you need to know?

▷ methods of storing cash, such as use of till, terminal and cash drawer

▷ cash handling techniques, including counting and giving change

▷ the use of a calculator

▷ financial calculations

▷ operation of credit card imprinters

▷ security and safety arrangements for handling money

▷ completion of forms and records

▷ VAT guidelines

▷ the implications of different forms of payment

BACKGROUND KNOWLEDGE

Payment for goods may be made in a number of different ways, most of which will be familiar to you.

Legal tender in the UK is any value of Bank of England notes or coins which, if offered within the limits of legal tender, must be accepted in settlement of the debt owed.

A **cheque** is an order to a banker to pay a sum of money to a named person or to his/her order. A specimen signature must be given to the bank. Most companies ask for a valid cheque card before accepting cheques in payment for goods.

Cheque cards guarantee that a cheque will be covered by the bank, usually for amounts up to £50 or £100, provided that the signatures on both match, and that the card date has not expired. The cheque card bears the signature of the account holder. The person accepting the card must check that it is current and has the correct signature, that the limit is not exceeded and, finally, that the account is not on the 'stop' list of cards.

Credit cards are issued by the banks to customers with good credit ratings. The two largest schemes are Barclaycard/Visa and Access.

Credit cards may be used to withdraw cash at any bank branch. There is an immediate interest charge for this service. They may also be used to obtain credit for goods and services. A special multicopy voucher is completed by the accepting party by inserting the embossed credit card and voucher into an imprinter which records details of the credit card account. The customer will sign the voucher and will receive a monthly statement of transactions and a time limit for payment.

If the amount owing is paid in full before the time limit expires, then no interest is charged. If less than the full amount is paid, then interest is charged on the remainder. In addition, some credit card companies make a small monthly charge on each account.

EFTPOS (electronic funds transfer at point of sale) is a card payment scheme installed at scanning checkouts in many stores. The system is linked to the customer's current account, which is debited within a few days with the amount spent. It is faster and more convenient than writing cheques. Cheque cards with a special SWITCH symbol are required to use this method of payment.

THE TASKS

TASK 1	Find out the limit set on the use of coins for legal tender in the UK.
TASK 2	Give five advantages to a customer of paying for goods or services by cheque
TASK 3	When accepting a cheque in payment for goods or services, how would you check its validity?
TASK 4	State the procedures you would follow if offered a credit card in payment for goods or services.
TASK 5	What features should be incorporated into a cash register to safeguard against pilfering on the till?
TASK 6	(a) Write down what the numbered labels on the cheque below are. (b) State which numbers you would check against a cheque card before accepting the cheque in payment for goods/services.

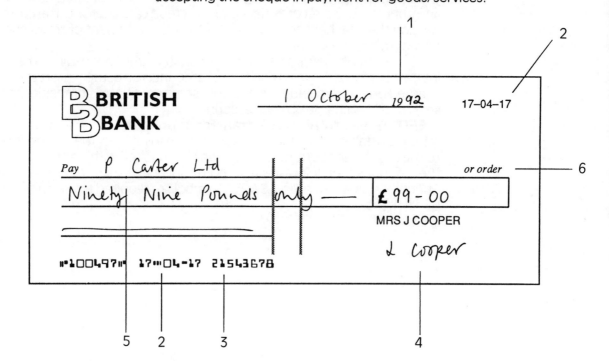

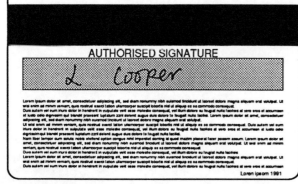

Cheque and cheque card

ELEMENT 20.3 *Prepare for routine banking transactions*

INTRODUCTION

What do you have to do?

▷ prepare for routine banking transactions

How well do you have to do it?

To achieve this you must be able to:

▷ complete all paying-in and withdrawal documents correctly

▷ calculate money correctly

▷ follow security procedures at all times

▷ identify all discrepancies and deal with them in accordance with laid-down procedures

▷ keep records up to date, legibly and accurately

What do you need to know?

▷ the procedures and documentation used by organisations

▷ banking services and procedures, arrangements and documentation

▷ security arrangements for money, including storage and transfer to and from banks

▷ foreign currency/currency exchange

▷ how to do financial calculations, including the use of the calculator

▷ how to complete forms/records

▷ how to plan and organise work within deadlines

What do you need to be able to do?

▷ complete paying-in procedures for cash, postal orders, cheques and credit card payments, including bagging-up and cash analysis

▷ prepare cheques, including the acquisition of foreign currency, for specific amounts, involving the analysis of requirements

▷ check all documentation for paying in or withdrawing money from the bank

BACKGROUND KNOWLEDGE

Most companies use a **current account** for their everyday banking requirements. Deposits and withdrawals may be made at any time and the company will be issued with a cheque book and paying-in book. Before money is paid into a current account it must be counted and bagged into packets, which the bank will supply.

Cheques, postal orders, credit cards, travellers cheques etc. should be examined closely before being accepted. Only then should they be entered on to a **paying-in slip**, together with the cash amounts, and paid into the bank. The total will also be entered on the counterfoil and kept as a record of the amount paid in. Details of cheques etc. will be listed on the back of the paying-in slip.

When withdrawing money from a current account it is usual to write a **cheque**, which is a request to the banker to pay from a current account a specified sum of money to the named person, or to the bearer. The most common way of safeguarding a cheque is to cross it – this means that the cheque can only be paid into a bank account. A further safeguard is to use a special crossing which restricts unauthorised use of the cheque even further – for example, 'A/C payee only' across the face of the cheque.

Cheque guarantee cards are generally requested when goods are bought with a cheque. This card guarantees that the bank will honour the cheque up to a specified amount. The cheque card also allows the bearer to withdraw a specified amount of cash (usually £50/£100) from any branch of the bank issuing the card. Cheque cards may also be used to withdraw cash from cashpoint machines. Most of the major banks have reciprocal arrangements with each other, which means that customers with cheque cards can get cash at almost any time and in any place in this country and abroad.

Credit transfers are useful in allowing people without bank accounts to pay their bills directly into the banking account of companies, such as the electricity companies and the gas board. These companies print a detachable credit transfer form at the bottom of their bills, which the customer can complete and take with the cash to the bank. A small service charge is made. The money paid on the bill will go directly into the banking account of the company. Bank account holders can simply complete the form and send it to the company, or take it with a cheque to the bank. No charge is made for this service.

Companies with a large number of accounts to settle (for instance, the wages) will complete a credit transfer for each account and then make out a duplicate credit transfer schedule, which lists all the payments made. These will be sent to the bank together with one cheque for the total amount of all the payments, and the monies will be transferred from the company account into the individual accounts named on the credit transfers.

Postal orders, which are obtainable from any post office, may be used to pay amounts between 25p and £20. The Post Office charges poundage, in proportion to the amount of the postal order. This method of payment for small amounts is becoming increasingly popular with companies that have had difficulty with payments by cheque. Crossing postal orders ensures that they must go through a bank account, thus increasing security.

Security precautions are very important when transporting cash between banks and workplaces. Some simple precautions will help to prevent problems. There should always be at least two people transporting the cash, which should be placed in a secure container. Routes and times should be varied as often as possible and the number of people who know of the changes should be restricted. If large sums of money are to be transported it may be advisable to employ a security company.

THE TASKS

Resources required by students/trainees

▷ Task 5 – an up-to-date list of currency exchange rates from a daily newspaper

TASK 1

Before cash is paid into a bank it must be counted and put into packets or bags provided by the bank. What amounts are acceptable for the following notes and coins?

£50, £20, £10, £5, £1, 50p, 20p, 10p, 5p, 2p, 1p

TASK 2

(a) What are the main differences between standing orders and direct debits?

(b) Which would you choose to pay quarterly electricity bills?

TASK 3

What do the following terms mean in connection with cheques?

stopped, blank, postdated, stale, dishonoured

TASK 4

Describe how, when and why you would use a postal order.

TASK 5

You are taking a business trip to Rome and estimate you will require £1000 for expenses. You will pay for your hotel with American Express and your travel expenses have been paid.

(a) How will you ensure that your £1000 is readily available in Italian currency and is also secure?

(b) Use the correct exchange rate to calculate how much foreign currency you will obtain for your £1000, and any charges which will be made for changing the money.

ELEMENT 20.4 *Make payments to suppliers and others*

INTRODUCTION

What do you have to do?

▷ make payments to suppliers and others

How well do you have to do it?

To achieve this you must be able to:

▷ prepare authorised payments using either manual or computerised systems to pay bills, invoices and expenses claims

▷ check for errors on all documents

▷ prepare cheques for signature, including counterfoils

▷ reconcile invoices, credit notes and statements

What do you need to know?

▷ the procedures and documentation used by organisations

▷ authorisation procedures

▷ allowable discounts

▷ the use of a calculator and financial calculations

▷ VAT guidelines

What do you need to be able to do?

▷ check all payment requests for accuracy and authorisation

▷ identify all discrepancies and/or errors and report them promptly

▷ prepare all cheques correctly

▷ prepare remittance advices accurately and despatch them with payment

▷ despatch all authorised payments to the correct recipient or location within defined time constraints

BACKGROUND KNOWLEDGE

Before making payments it is important to check that goods or services have been received, discounts have been deducted where applicable, and payments have been authorised.

THE TASKS

Resources required by students/trainees

You will each require photocopies of the following:

▷ Task 1 – the blank cheque – one copy

▷ Task 2 – the statement of account – one copy

TASK 1   An authorised expenses claim form is shown below. Using the blank cheque and counterfoil provided, complete the cheque required to pay this claim.

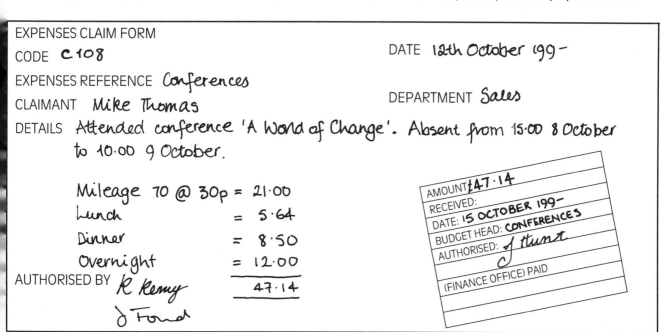

EXPENSES CLAIM FORM

CODE **C 108**

EXPENSES REFERENCE *Conferences*

CLAIMANT *Mike Thomas*

DATE *12th October 199‒*

DEPARTMENT *Sales*

DETAILS *Attended conference 'A World of Change'. Absent from 15.00 8 October to 10.00 9 October.*

Mileage 70 @ 30p =	21.00
Lunch =	5.64
Dinner =	8.50
Overnight =	12.00
AUTHORISED BY *R Kenny*	47.14
J Ford	

AMOUNT £47.14
RECEIVED:
DATE: 15 OCTOBER 199‒
BUDGET HEAD: CONFERENCES
AUTHORISED: *J Hunt*

(FINANCE OFFICE) PAID

An authorised expenses claim form

TASK 2   Refer to the incoming invoices record sheet for Townslee Publishing on page 94.

Complete the statement of account provided, which Townslee Publishing will send to J.C. Hunt & Co. Townslee Publishing received a cheque for £5000 on 9 October and sent a credit note against invoice TP7583, dated 2 October, for £176.25 on 16 October.

How would Townslee Publishing show the 'Returned to sender' items on the statement?

What action would J.C. Hunt expect them to take with regard to these items?

J.C. HUNT & CO.

INCOMING INVOICES RECORD SHEET

RS = Return to Sender
PC = Passed to Cashier

Date	Invoice number	Supplier	Invoice total £	Cost of goods £	VAT £	Action RS PC
Oct 2	TP7583	Townslee Publishing	176-25	150-00	26-25	RS
5	TP7611	''	219-72	187-00	32-72	PC
9	TP8129	''	493-50	420-00	73-50	PC
12	TP8213	''	41-99	35-74	6-25	RS
18	TP8298	''	193-87	165-00	28-87	PC
19	TP8310	''	188-00	160-00	28-00	PC
21	TP8422	''	9-97	8-49	1-48	PC
24	TP8483	''	782-49	665-95	116-54	RS
29	TP8534	''	42-79	36-42	6-37	PC
30	TP8900	''	31-16	26-52	4-64	PC
		TOTAL	2179.76	1855-12	324-64	

UNIT 21

ELEMENT 21.1 *Reconcile incoming invoices for payment*

INTRODUCTION

What do you have to do?

▷ reconcile incoming invoices for payment

How well do you have to do it?

To achieve this you must be able to:

▷ check invoices against orders and delivery notes and identify and report discrepancies

▷ identify and report all errors on invoices

▷ rectify all errors and discrepancies as directed

▷ pass correct and authorised invoices for payment

▷ investigate and report or resolve all queries

▷ keep records up to date and legible

▷ disclose information only to authorised persons

What do you need to know?

▷ the functions of purchasing, sales and accounts departments in a company

▷ how to use VAT guidelines, price lists and catalogues

▷ how to identify the different types of discount

▷ the procedures and documentation used in organisations

▷ filing systems

▷ the importance of confidentiality

▷ how to perform financial calculations, including the use of a calculator

▷ how to communicate effectively

▷ how to plan and organise work within deadlines

What do you need to be able to do?

▷ record details of incoming invoices as directed

▷ check incoming invoices for accuracy against orders and delivery notes

▷ pass invoices forward for certification and payment

▷ draft and, after approval and signature, despatch letters of complaint or query where necessary

BACKGROUND KNOWLEDGE

Before attempting Element 21.1, you should either complete all the tasks in Unit 4, Element 2 *Process incoming invoices for payment*, or provide evidence that you can meet all the criteria required for that element.

Businesses generally exist to make a profit by either manufacturing, selling, advising or offering a service. In order to ensure the business operates efficiently, records of all transactions must be kept. The number and style of records will depend upon the size of the company.

In a small company all the records will probably be kept by one person, but larger companies will have specialist departments dealing with each part of a transaction. The larger the company, the more departments it is likely to have.

There are, however, departments common to all companies involved in offering goods/services for sale, which are of particular importance to this unit of work:

Purchasing	Sales	Accounts
Requisition	Catalogue	Cash paid out
	Price list	Cash received
Enquiry	Quotation	Petty cash
Order	Advice note	Company account
Delivery note	Accounts received	
Goods received		Accounts payable
	Invoice	Payroll
	Statement	Fixed assets
		Cost control
Payment		Credit control

Documents used in business transactions

The purchasing department of a company wishing to buy goods will usually send an **enquiry** to a number of suppliers. In return they will receive **catalogues**, **price lists** and **quotations** from which to make their choice. The quotation will give the price of goods plus details of delivery and any trade or cash discounts offered.

Trade discount is a reduction on the stated price of an article. It is given to enable the buyer to make a profit on the catalogue price if s/he resells the goods.

Cash discount is an allowance given to the buyer for payment within a fixed period and is usually given to encourage prompt payment of bills.

When a firm buys goods on credit it will receive an **invoice** from the seller of the goods. To the seller it is a **sales invoice** and will be recorded in the sales day book. To the buyer the same invoice is a **purchase invoice** and will be recorded in the purchases day book.

The net amount of the purchase invoice is listed in the purchases day book and the items are then posted to the credit of the personal accounts in the purchases ledger. The invoices are then filed. At the end of the period the total of the purchases book is transferred to the debit of the purchases account in the general ledger.

Invoices are entered exactly as received throughout the book-keeping system and are corrected later by credit or debit entries. Many companies have computerised the control of day books and ledgers and there are many excellent software packages available for both large and small companies.

Firms with a turnover above £35,000 will be involved in the payment of Value Added Tax (VAT). Guidelines on VAT are available free of charge from the local Customs and Excise Office. As VAT is a tax levied on the value added to goods at every stage from the natural product until it reaches the final customer, it is important that an **output tax record** is kept of VAT added to the charges made to customers for goods/services. An **input tax record** must also be kept of all VAT charges made on the business by suppliers. The business only has to pay the difference between the input tax and the output tax to the Customs and Excise.

Companies selling zero rated goods (e.g. goods which are being exported directly from the UK to overseas countries) do not add VAT to the selling price of their goods but ARE allowed to obtain a refund on VAT paid by them on goods/services provided the company is registered for VAT.

Some goods/services are exempt from VAT, such as food, postal services, insurance premiums and bank charges, and so are firms with a small turnover. Exempt firms cannot claim refunds on the VAT they pay to others.

A taxable firm will have to add VAT to the value of sales invoices. VAT is based on the amount of the invoice after trade discount and cash discount have been deducted. The formula used for calculating VAT is:

$$\frac{\text{cost of goods including VAT} \times \text{rate of tax}}{100 + \text{rate of tax}} = \text{amount of VAT paid}$$

For example:

$$\frac{£2.35 \text{ (goods including VAT)} \times 17.5}{117.5} = 35\text{p VAT}$$

THE TASKS

Resources required by students/trainees

You will each require photocopies of the following:

▷ Tasks 1 and 2 – the incoming invoices record sheet – one copy

TASK 1

You have received two invoices from 21 Club, both for:
Buffet supper for 40 on 5 October @ £4 per head = £160
plus VAT   £ 28

£188

dated 12 October number 464175
dated 12 October number 464298
   Take whatever actions are required to rectify this error. Enter both invoices on the incoming invoice record sheet.

TASK 2

You have received an invoice dated 12 October from PL Stationery Supplies for £306 to cover the purchase of twenty-four A5 Goldstar Binders made to order specially for you. However, on checking your order books you can trace no such order.
   Prepare a letter on your wordprocessor or typewriter to PL Stationery Supplies explaining what has happened and advising them of how they should rectify this error.
   Meanwhile enter the invoice on your incoming invoices record sheet.

TASK 3

Your company is computerising the accounts system and needs codes for all the expense headings. Can you suggest at least ten expense headings that a large company might use?

ELEMENT 21.2   *Prepare and despatch quotations, invoices and statements*

INTRODUCTION

What do you have to do?

▷ prepare and despatch quotations, invoices and statements

▷ file and distribute copies of documents

▷ keep all records up to date, legibly and accurately

▷ deal effectively with enquiries and complaints

▷ ensure confidentiality of information

How well do you have to do it?

To achieve this you must be able to:

▷ prepare a variety of quotations, invoices and statements on both manual and computerised systems

▷ process quotations, invoices and statements on both manual and computerised systems

▷ prepare statements which include invoice amounts, amounts paid, VAT and balance

▷ prepare routine and non-routine invoices

What do you need to know?

▷ the functions of purchasing, sales and accounts departments in a company

▷ the operation and use of manual and computerised accounting systems

▷ the use of VAT guidelines, price lists and catalogues

▷ how to identify the different types of discount

▷ the procedures and documentation used in organisations

▷ filing systems

▷ the importance of confidentiality at all times

▷ the reasons for using pro-forma invoices

▷ the justification for using credit control and how it can be applied

▷ the organisation's policy and authorised persons

What do you need to be able to do?

▷ prepare and issue quotations

▷ prepare and issue statements

▷ prepare invoices for despatch

BACKGROUND KNOWLEDGE

On receiving a suitable quotation the purchasing department will place an **order** for goods. The order is usually written or typed/wordprocessed on a standard form with a fixed number and sent out in numerical order. On receipt of the order the supplier will produce an **invoice**, which is in effect the bill for goods supplied and may be used in a court of law as evidence of a contract of sale of goods.

Invoices are generally multiple-copy documents produced on continuous stationery and carbonised paper. Colour coding is often used to distinguish the various uses of the copies:

1 The top copy is sent to the purchaser as a **bill and contract of sale**. The purchaser will process the invoice through the purchases day book.

2 The **second copy** will be kept by the seller and processed through the sales day book.

   Both these copies will contain full information on costs, discounts, deliveries and VAT.

3 The third copy will be sent in advance of the goods and is known as the **advice note**. This note advises the purchaser what goods to expect and notifies any shortages in the order.

4 The fourth copy is the **despatch note**. It contains the same details as the advice note but is kept by the seller to record progress on the order.

5 The fifth copy is the **delivery note** which is sent with the goods, signed by the purchaser after checking the goods and returned to the seller as proof of acceptance of the delivery of goods by the purchaser.

If the supplier makes an undercharge on the invoice, a **debit note** requesting extra payment is sent to the purchaser. This is treated in the same way as the invoice for book-keeping purposes and entered in the purchases day book by the purchaser.

If the supplier overcharges on the invoice, or if goods are damaged and returned etc., a **credit note** will be sent to the purchaser. This is usually printed in red and the purchaser will enter it into his/her purchases return book. A copy will be kept by the supplier, who will enter it into the sales return book.

The supplier will send **statements** to all purchasers, usually once a month, showing a record of all transactions in date order. The last item shows the amount due to the seller. When the statement is received the purchaser should check it against all invoices, credit/debit notes and payments made since the last statement, and if it is correct send payment to the supplier. If the statement is not settled, another copy will be sent to the purchaser.

Pro-forma invoices are used in the following circumstances:

• when goods are sent on approval, to inform the prospective buyer of the price and charges if the goods are accepted

• when a buyer is unknown, or has a history of poor settlement of accounts, the buyer will be required to settle the pro-forma before the goods are despatched

• as a declaration to the customs officials of the amount of goods being despatched abroad

THE TASKS

Resources required by students/trainees

You will each require photocopies of the following:

▷ Task 2 – the blank credit note

▷ Task 3 – the five enquiries; the two price lists; the blank quotation

▷ Task 4 – the five purchase orders; the blank invoice; the blank delivery note

TASK 1

Draw a diagram to illustrate the flow of documents between buyer and seller from the enquiry to the statement. State which departments in each company would be involved in the transactions.

TASK 2

(a) Draft a reply to a letter of complaint received from Stevens & Hewins of 51 Dickins Road, Grantham LN19 3AZ, which stated that the Whitehall range low-backed executive revolve and tilt chair with three-star upholstery was delivered in red and not in blue as per order number SH/987. Cost £188 plus VAT at $17\frac{1}{2}$%.

Type or wordprocess the final copy of the letter, which will be signed by the Sales Manager and should go out today.

(b) Using a photocopy of the blank credit note supplied, prepare a credit note to send with the letter.

(c) Take a copy of both letter and credit note for the cashier's section and one for your files.

(d) File your copy under the customer's name.

(e) Address an envelope and attach it to the credit note and letter.

TASK 3

You have been handed five enquiries:

(a) Take five photocopies of the blank quotation form provided.

(b) From the price lists provided, prepare quotations, dated and ready for signature, to be sent by return post. Number quotations sequentially.

(c) Take two photocopies of each quotation. Mark one copy for the accounts department and place it in the out tray. The other is for your own files.

(d) Prepare an envelope for the top copy of each quotation and attach it ready for signature.

(e) File your copies in numerical order.

TASK 4

Five orders were received and handed to you as a result of the quotations you sent out.

(a) Retrieve the quotations from the numerical file and check against the orders.

(b) Take a photocopy of each order for the accounts department files, and place the copies in the out tray.

(c) Make five photocopies of the blank invoice and delivery note. Prepare an invoice and delivery note for each customer. Make copies for the accounts department and despatch section, which you should place in the out tray, and one copy for your own files. Provide a suitable date for each form.

(d) File your copies in alphabetical order by customer's name.

(e) Address envelopes for each customer and attach them to the top copy of the invoices.

ELEMENT 21.3 *Process expenses claims for payment*

INTRODUCTION

What do you have to do?

▷ process expenses claims for payment

How well do you have to do it?

To achieve this you must be able to:

▷ identify and investigate all errors in expenses claims

▷ report all unresolved discrepancies and errors

▷ pass only authorised and correctly completed expenses for payment

▷ keep all records up to date, legibly and accurately

▷ maintain confidentiality of information at all times

What do you need to know?

▷ how to use organisation codes for dealing with reimbursement of expenses, including special and non-routine payments

▷ the use of VAT guidelines for recording taxable and non-taxable expenses

▷ how to use a calculator effectively

▷ the action to be taken with incorrect/inconsistent expenses claims

What do you need to be able to do?

▷ allocate expenses to appropriate expenses codes

▷ check expenses claims for accuracy, validity and authorisation against approved codes

▷ deal with incorrect/inconsistent claim forms

▷ investigate and resolve discrepancies

▷ calculate VAT

▷ complete all records accurately

▷ maintain confidentiality at all times

▷ communicate effectively

BACKGROUND KNOWLEDGE

The method of claiming expenses generally differs according to the size of claim being made. Most companies have a 'cut-off' level, and if the claim is below this it can be made through petty cash, but if it is larger, it can only be made through the normal invoice payment procedures.

A petty cash voucher is used for the reimbursement of small amounts and usually only requires one authorised signature to allow the cashier to make the payment. Normally the person receiving the money will have to sign the slip to acknowledge receipt of the money.

Other expenses claims come in all kinds of layout, colour and size; normally receipts for purchases, hotel bills, proof of travel etc. will be attached when submitting the claim. The claim is usually treated like any other incoming invoice and goes through the normal authorisation and control procedure. The claimant will in due course receive payment, usually by cheque.

Many companies now have a company credit card (such as American Express) for their management personnel. This makes it easier and more convenient for staff to pay expenses, and in due course the company receives one bill highlighting the individual expenses incurred. Expenses are generally not tax deductible although there are a few exceptions, such as certain entertaining expenses, clothing allowances and some research and development expenses. VAT at standard rate is payable on most expenses.

VAT formula: the following is the formula for calculating VAT:

$$\frac{\text{cost of goods including VAT} \times \text{rate of tax}}{100 + \text{rate of tax}} = \text{amount of VAT paid}$$

For example,

$$\frac{\text{£2.35 (goods including VAT)} \times 17.5}{117.5} = \text{35p (VAT)}$$

THE TASK

Resources required by students/trainees

You will each require photocopies of the following:

▷ The twenty expenses forms – one copy

Expenses, codes, references and approved authorisations

Code	Expenses reference	Authorisation
1022/1	Travel	D. Osborne
1022/2	Subsistence	K. Kenny
1022/3	Mileage	J. Ford
2133/1	Hospitality	T. Floyd
2133/2	Training	A. Scholy
3291/1	Equipment	I. Bottrill
3291/2	Publicity	M. Booker
3291/3	Catering costs	B. Cook

Expenses allowances

Car allowance 30p per mile up to 30 miles
20p per mile above 30 miles

Subsistence
Absence	0700–0900	Breakfast	£3.20
	1200–1400	Lunch	£5.64
	1800–2100	Dinner	£8.50
	Overnight allowance		£12.00

All overnight claims must be countersigned by J. Mulholland, Cashier.

Expenses over £100 must be countersigned by K. MacDonagh, Director.

Items under £5 should be claimed on petty cash through your own department.

Information required for Task 1

TASK 1

Obtain your own photocopies of the twenty expenses claim forms. Complete the expenses forms as follows:

(a) Insert the correct codes using the information provided above (ask for advice if you are unsure).

(b) Insert the correct expenses references.

(c) Check the signatures.

(d) Check the totals.

ELEMENT 21.4 *Order office goods and services*

INTRODUCTION

What do you have to do?

▷ draft and despatch letters of enquiry, giving precise, specified requirements

▷ obtain quotations

▷ prepare orders and complete records correctly

▷ maintain stock at agreed levels

▷ keep records up to date, legibly and accurately

How well do you have to do it?

To achieve this you must be able to:

▷ use sources of supply, such as catalogues and price lists

▷ compile letters of enquiry for stationery and office equipment

▷ give precise, specified requirements for different items

▷ use oral or written communication to obtain quotations

▷ compare the received information for quantity, quality and cost

▷ store information, using the appropriate filing method

▷ correctly draft and send orders for materials

▷ complete stock records accurately

▷ keep stock records up to date, legibly and accurately

▷ estimate future requirement levels according to demand and availability

▷ use imperial and metric units

▷ organise servicing contracts for equipment

▷ arrange agency staff cover

What do you need to know?

▷ the types of material and service used

▷ where to find sources of supply, such as catalogues and price lists

▷ how to draft letters

▷ how to communicate orally, by telephone and in writing

▷ tendering procedures in an organisation

▷ how to select and compare relevant information

▷ the organisation's policy on quantity, quality and cost

▷ how to select particular supplies

▷ the filing systems for stock records

▷ how to complete orders and stock cards

▷ the procedure for emergency orders

▷ how to keep stock records up to date

▷ how to estimate and calculate future requirements based on demand and availability

▷ the difference between imperial and metric units

What do you need to be able to do?

▷ complete letters of enquiry

▷ obtain quotations for stationery and office equipment

▷ arrange servicing contracts for office equipment

▷ use communication equipment, such as facsimile, telex and telephone

▷ store information and compare prices

▷ prepare and despatch orders

▷ process emergency orders

▷ complete and update stock cards

▷ maintain stock levels

▷ work out costs for imperial and metric units

▷ organise agency staff cover

BACKGROUND KNOWLEDGE

In an organisation, stock is held in store to be used at some time in the future. This stock consists of raw materials, spare parts, items used to run the business such as paper and envelopes, goods bought to be resold eventually, and finished goods.

All this stock has a money value as it has been bought, and it will cost money to replace any that goes missing, so care must be taken of it. If a business runs out of an item such as bond paper that is necessary to complete office work, staff cannot work properly because the materials are not available. So businesses need stock control.

Records are kept to show how many of each item are in stock, where to order them from and how quickly they can be obtained. It is important that stock is ordered in good time so that it does not run out or get low. Records also help to show up goods which are not being used regularly.

These records can be kept manually or computerised. Stock is physically checked at regular intervals so that the Accounts Department can find out what the stock is worth, and also to monitor pilfering, wastage or damage.

Stock control cards

A stock record is kept for each item, showing the description, colour, supplier, maximum and minimum stock to be kept, and reorder level (when more supplies must be ordered).

The **balance in stock** figure is the amount of goods in stock. A record is kept of what has come in (**receipts**), what has gone out (**issues**) and what has been ordered from the supplier. These stock records are checked against what is in store when a stock check is made.

Requisitions

Requisitions are documents completed by people in the business who want stationery and office equipment items from the store. It is used as a receipt when the goods are issued. It has to be authorised by a person in authority.

Enquiries

Enquiries are made by firms for goods they wish to buy, and also for details of price and delivery date. They may also ask for leaflets or brochures. Enquiries can be in the form of letters, forms or telexes. They can be sent by post or facsimile. Enquiries can also be made orally by telephone.

Quotations

Quotations are received from other companies in response to enquiries. They give details of goods to be sold and include quantity, description, catalogue number, price and delivery details. These quotations are compared by the Purchasing Officer before deciding which goods to buy.

Orders

These are forms which are sent by the Purchasing Officer to order goods when it has been decided to purchase new materials. They are based on the details of the quotations and are numbered and dated. A copy is sent to the Accounts Department.

If an item is required urgently, it may be necessary to place an **emergency order** over the telephone. In this case it is important to follow the correct procedure for your organisation, and an order number should be obtained from the Purchasing Officer to give over the telephone. The order should be confirmed in writing as soon as possible. It is important to keep sufficient stocks in store so that emergency orders are not normally needed.

When ordering large items of office equipment, such as photocopiers, fax machines and computers, it is important to put the orders **out to tender**. Several suppliers should be contacted and asked to quote for the item.

In deciding which quotation to accept, you must take into account the running costs and servicing contracts when deciding on the most economical buy. For instance, when purchasing a photocopier, it has to be decided whether to lease or buy the equipment, and the servicing costs and cost per copy have to be taken into account.

The **depreciation** of the equipment is also a factor. If you feel you may need to change equipment regularly to update it to your changing needs, you may decide it is better to lease than to buy.

It may be necessary to organise staff cover with an employment agency to undertake the work of personnel who are off sick or on holiday. In this case it is necessary to contact several local agencies to find out the cost of hiring staff and whether the staff you need are available.

THE TASKS

Resources required by students/trainees

You will each require photocopies of the following:

▷ Task 1 (a) – the enquiry form – one copy

▷ Task 3 – the order form – one copy

▷ Task 4 – the stock record card – one copy

▷ Task 5 – the stock requisition – one copy

TASK 1

(a) You work for MacDonagh & Sons, 19 Commander Close, Wakefield, Yorkshire WA7 4DR, tel. 0924 918761, fax 0924 05371. Your firm is considering purchasing some special ring binders for storing forms. These should be 9″ × 7″ and red in colour. Complete the enquiry form provided, for details of these ring binders, and send to:

W. Green & Sons
Office Stationery Supplies
330 Goodge Street
CAMBRIDGE
Cambs
CB4 4DW

(b) Draft a letter of enquiry for ring binders. You are interested in an initial purchase of 100 binders, and need supplies within two weeks. Send the letter to:

The Topstat Company,
7 Western Avenue,
HARLOW
Essex
CM17 9LH

TASK 2

As a result of your enquiries, the following two quotations have been received. Compare the prices and delivery dates and decide which company you will order from. Open a file for each company.

```
                            QUOTATION
      To

      MacDonagh & Sons              W Green & Sons
      19 Commander Close            Office Stationery Supplier
      WAKEFIELD                     330 Goodge Street
      Yorkshire                     CAMBRIDGE
      WA7 4DR                       CB4 4DW

                                    Date: 11 February 199-


      Dear Sirs

      With reference to your enquiry, we give below our terms and
      prices, as requested.

      100 9" x 7" red ring binders at 0.62p each

      Delivery - 3 weeks

      Terms nett

      Yours faithfully

      H. Guild

      Sales Department
```

Quotation for Task 2

```
                         QUOTATION
   To

   MacDonagh & Sons              The Topstat Company
   19 Commander Close            7 Western Avenue
   WAKEFIELD                     HARLOW
   Yorkshire                     Essex
   WA7 4DR                       CM14 9LH

                                 Date: 11 February 199-


   Dear Sirs

   We have pleasure in quoting you as follows:-

   100 9" x 7" red ring binders at 0.56p each

   Delivery ex stock - 2 weeks

   Terms 10% - 21 days

   Yours faithfully

   W Jones

   W Jones
   Sales
```

Quotation for Task 2

TASK 3 Complete the blank order form provided to the company of your choice, for the purchase of 100 9" × 7" red ring binders at the cost they quote for each binder. Work out the cost of this. The order number is 0001, dated 12 February 199–, delivery required by 26 February 199–.

TASK 4 Complete the stock record card provided. The stock number is 310. The maximum stock should be 100 binders.
   To work out the minimum stock level, use the average weekly consumption × (delivery period + one week). The weekly consumption of binders is ten and the delivery period is two weeks. Enter the minimum stock level on the stock card.
   The reorder level should be 40.
   Also enter the details of the order.

TASK 5 The order for the ring binders is received on 23 February 199–, invoice number 4671. Enter the details on the stock record card; the balance in stock will be 100.
   On 6 March the Accounts Department sends a requisition, number 1, for twelve binders. Complete the requisition form and work out the cost for the department. Work out the size of each binder in millimetres and enter all details on the requisition. There are 25 millimetres to the inch.
   Enter details of the requisition on the stock record card and amend the balance in stock.

ELEMENT 22.1 *Process documentation for wages and salaries*

ELEMENT 22.2 *Process direct payment of wages and salaries*

ELEMENT 22.3 *Arrange credit transfers*

In this unit the three elements have been integrated wherever possible because of their close relationship in the working situation.

INTRODUCTION

What do you have to do?

▷ calculate pay deductions and produce pay advice slips

▷ record wages paid, and complete statutory records and returns

▷ prepare wage packets, including cash analysis and cheque preparation

▷ arrange credit transfers for the payment of wages and salaries

How well do you have to do it?

To achieve this you must be able to:

▷ calculate pay correctly using tax tables, maternity pay and sick pay reference books

▷ prepare pay advice slips and other records

▷ arrange for wages and salaries to be paid in cash, by cheque, or by credit transfer

▷ understand the need for statutory returns and complete them correctly

▷ handle pay queries tactfully and courteously

▷ explain the need for confidentiality and security

What do you need to know?

▷ how to calculate pay both manually and on computers

▷ the significance of tax codes

▷ how to use tax and National Insurance (NI) tables as reference books in the calculation of pay

▷ how to process other deductions, such as attachment of earnings and pensions

▷ how to deal with statutory sick pay (SSP), statutory maternity pay (SMP) and holiday pay

▷ what records need to be completed and what each type of record is used for

▷ the available methods for paying employees

What do you need to be able to do?

▷ calculate hours worked and pay including bonuses, overtime or commission

▷ use standard tables to calculate tax and NI

▷ deal with pensions, SSP, SMP and holiday pay

▷ calculate net pay

▷ record calculations in wages books, on tax cards and in pay slip booklets

▷ produce pay advice slips

▷ complete statutory returns

▷ do a cash analysis to prepare cash wage packets

▷ write out pay cheques correctly

▷ issue pay packets and obtain signatures for receipt

▷ arrange credit transfers to pay wages directly into employees' bank accounts

▷ deal with pay queries

▷ complete forms for employees (such as P45 and P60)

BACKGROUND KNOWLEDGE

Most employees are paid a wage or salary of a fixed amount, although some will receive extra money for **overtime** (often at a higher rate of pay), or **commission** on goods sold (as salespeople do) or **bonuses** (for instance, for high productivity).

All earnings are subject to **tax** and to **National Insurance (NI)** contributions, although a fixed amount of an employee's income is free of tax. This figure can be calculated from the employee's **tax code**. Tax and NI are deducted from wages as they are paid, so that employees cannot run up a huge bill which they cannot meet at the end of the tax year. This system, which is run by employers for their employees, is called **Pay As You Earn (PAYE)**.

Employees are paid either weekly or, more commonly these days, monthly. The financial year for tax purposes runs from 6 April to 5 April, no matter on what day employees are paid. April is called month 1 and March is called month 12.

The employer has to calculate hours worked for hourly paid staff, and hence the **basic pay**. Overtime, bonuses and commission are all additional payments which employees might be entitled to, and which have to be calculated and added to basic pay.

The tax and NI contributions due are calculated using standard tables which all employers receive from their local **Inland Revenue** (tax) office. Other alterations to pay may include contributions to a pension scheme, statutory sick pay (SSP) which is paid when an employee is away sick for more than three days, statutory maternity pay (SMP) which is paid to women on maternity leave, and holiday pay.

These details are recorded in a **wages book** (sometimes called a wages summary book), on **deductions working sheets** (**P11** forms) and on a **pay advice slip** which is given to the employee. Wages can be paid in cash, by cheque, or by bank credit transfer directly into the employee's bank or building society account. Credit transfers may also be used for purposes other than paying salaries and may be used to move money to pay for goods or services abroad.

Each month (by the 19th) the tax office expects to receive the tax and NI that the employer has collected from employees. The figures are entered into a **pay slip booklet P30BC(Z)** which is kept by the employer, and also on to a **pay slip P30B(Z)** which is sent with a cheque to the tax office at Shipley or Cumbernauld.

At the end of each tax year, the employer needs to complete the triplicate form P14 for each employee. The third copy of this is the **certificate of pay and tax deducted (P60)** which is given to the employee as a summary of his/her tax and NI for the year. The top two copies are for the Department of Social Security (DSS) and the Inland Revenue. These are sent to the tax office with a completed **P35** form, which is a summary deductions working sheet.

If an employee leaves the company during the tax year, the employer needs to issue **details of employee leaving (P45)**. The employees give this to their new employers to help them calculate their tax correctly.

THE TASKS

The tasks (and assignments) for Elements 22.1, 22.2 and 22.3 are set and assessed together because of the close links between them.

Resources required by students/trainees

You can each photocopy the following as needed from the *Tutor's Resource Pack*:

▷ Tasks 1–6 the blank page from the wages book; the blank cheque, the blank pay advice slip

▷ Task 7 – the P11 form for Mr A.B. Smith

▷ Tasks 8 and 9 – the blank memo form

You will also require:

▷ Tasks 1–6 P11 forms; a pay slip booklet (P30BC(Z); a Girobank slip P30B(Z); a credit transfer form; P45 and P35 forms

▷ Task 7 – a blank P45 form

Scenario

Soft Soap (see Unit 3, Element 3 *Update records in a computerised database*) has twenty-one employees. The Managing Director, Mr Raj, has a Personal Assistant, Ms Jones, and an Accounts Clerk, Mr A. Smith, working for him.

There is a Personnel Officer and her assistant, a Publicity Manager, a Graphics Design Artist, an Office Supervisor, two typists, and an office junior.

There are five salespeople who also do some packing and deliveries, and there are two factory workers who mix and bottle the products and prepare orders, which are packaged by two packers/deliverers.

All are paid monthly, although the factory workers record their hours on time sheets, because they receive overtime on any hours over 30 per week, and the salespeople receive commission on goods sold.

You are Susan Jones, the Personal Assistant to Mr Raj. It is your responsibility to calculate the wages each month, and to prepare the cheques for signing by the company's accountants. You also have to fill in the statutory forms for the Inland Revenue.

DATA ON EMPLOYEES *for Tasks 1–6*

Job	Surname	Forenames	Salary (£)	Monthly (£)	NI number	DoB	Works no	Tax code	Bank sort code	A/c
Managing Director	Raj	Surinder Singh	24,000	2,000	PR 37 96 28 C	080850	80700	230T	23-12-08	29652685
Accounts Clerk	Smith	Abel B.	18,000	1,500	YF 34 56 78 A	020360	80702	242T	60-02-01	58627937
Personal Assistant	Jones	Susan K.	15,000	1,250	CR 98 23 56 B	190747	80701	242T	15-07-12	73972854
Sales	Challis	Robert	9,900	825	YC 32 14 56 X	240467	80703	200T	59-08-31	45834686
	Mather	James	9,120	760	BC 44 54 34 X	291166	80704	379T	62-10-07	64316794
	Peters	Alice	10,200	850	YC 21 67 93 D	160566	80705	242T	62-10-67	15458629
	Kennedy	Edward	9,000	750	SP 12 78 36 D	120769	80706	320T	23-12-08	92456378
Factory Workers	White	Janice	8,940	745	SR 47 38 91 P	170970	80707	242T	15-07-12	86745935
	Singh	Ravinder	14,700	1,225	BC 56 12 34 F	040448	80708	242T	62-10-07	32289745
	Oak	Simon	8,400	700	XY 32 14 96 F	160570	80709	379H	59-08-31	57796244
Personnel Officer	Virk	Jasvinder Singh	13,500	1125	PQ 51 24 96 R	080760	80710	242T	15-07-12	21867821
Personnel Assistant	Collins	Alan	11,100	925	NR 31 45 12 C	190967	80711	335T	60-02-01	42964876
Publicity Manager	Yen	Lee Sui	12,000	1,000	RT 27 38 49 T	231261	80712	242T	18-09-08	81442876
Graphics Design	Relton	Robert	10,500	875	SR 19 28 83 C	030371	80713	380H	36-12-14	91978546
Office Junior	Jolly	Paul	6,450	537.50	BS 21 42 11 R	140572	80714	278L	62-10-07	80876885
Office Supervisor	Clarke	Amanda	9,750	812.50	PR 13 97 46 T	121258	80715	242T	59-08-31	47266541
Typists	Hemel	Lloyd	7,350	612.50	FB 51 32 67 R	070169	80716	350H	63-12-05	14567654
	Doyle	Helen	8,700	725	NN 72 83 94 T	140748	80717	242T	15-07-12	26747569
	Trivet	Jeff	7,500	625	BF 91 82 38 C	120970	80718	242T	62-10-07	76478608
Packers	Morgan	Ada	7,800	650	RP 31 23 49 T	010263	80719	230T	62-10-07	13228765

MONTHLY COMMISSION AND OVERTIME PAYMENTS
for Tasks 1–6

Details of additional pay (commission and overtime payments)

	Commission					Overtime		
	R. Challis	J. Mather	A. Peters	E. Kennedy	J. White	R. Singh	S. Oak	
						Hours at: £12 per hour	£9 per hour	
	£	£	£	£	£			
April	69	20	23	10	33	7	8	April
May	80	16	36	15	37	9	6	May
June	62	25	15	29	20	8	7	June
July	95	39	62	12	58	11	10	July
August	98	46	22	37	10	5	3	August
September	71	65	33	10	38	7	5	September
October	66	13	40	45	30	9	8	October
November	61	35	17	40	51	12	10	November
December	21	35	24	60	20	9	8	December
January	50	17	54	38	33	10	6	January
February	47	20	45	13	35	8	6	February
March	62.5	13.2	0	12	15	9	8	March

DIARY FOR THE YEAR   *for reference purposes*

APRIL
M T W T F S S
1 2 3 4 5 6 7
8 9 10 11 12 13 14
15 16 17 18 19 20 21
22 23 24 25 26 27 28
29 30

MAY
M T W T F S S
1 2 3 4 5
6 7 8 9 10 11 12
13 14 15 16 17 18 19
20 21 22 23 24 25 26
27 28 29 30 31

JUNE
M T W T F S S
1 2
3 4 5 6 7 8 9
10 11 12 13 14 15 16
17 18 19 20 21 22 23
24 25 26 27 28 29 30

JULY
M T W T F S S
1 2 3 4 5 6 7
8 9 10 11 12 13 14
15 16 17 18 19 20 21
22 23 24 25 26 27 28
29 30 31

AUGUST
M T W T F S S
1 2 3 4
5 6 7 8 9 10 11
12 13 14 15 16 17 18
19 20 21 22 23 24 25
26 27 28 29 30 31

SEPTEMBER
M T W T F S S
1
2 3 4 5 6 7 8
9 10 11 12 13 14 15
16 17 18 19 20 21 22
23 24 25 26 27 28 29
30

OCTOBER
M T W T F S S
1 2 3 4 5 6
7 8 9 10 11 12 13
14 15 16 17 18 19 20
21 22 23 24 25 26 27
28 29 30 31

NOVEMBER
M T W T F S S
1 2 3
4 5 6 7 8 9 10
11 12 13 14 15 16 17
18 19 20 21 22 23 24
25 26 27 28 29 30

DECEMBER
M T W T F S S
1
2 3 4 5 6 7 8
9 10 11 12 13 14 15
16 17 18 19 20 21 22
23 24 25 26 27 28 29
30 31

JANUARY
M T W T F S S
1 2 3 4 5 6
7 8 9 10 11 12 13
14 15 16 17 18 19 20
21 22 23 24 25 26 27
28 29 30 31

FEBRUARY
M T W T F S S
1 2 3
4 5 6 7 8 9 10
11 12 13 14 15 16 17
18 19 20 21 22 23 24
25 26 27 28

MARCH
M T W T F S S
1 2 3
4 5 6 7 8 9 10
11 12 13 14 15 16 17
18 19 20 21 22 23 24
25 26 27 28 29 30 31

Month 1 (6 April–5 May)
No variations.

Month 2 (6 May–5 June)
Robert Relton is off sick from 8 May and returns to work on 22 May.

Month 3 (6 June–5 July)
Jeff Trivet is off sick from 14 June and returns on 21 June.

Month 4 (6 July–5 August)
No variations.

Month 5 (6 August–5 September)
Lee Sui Yen is off sick from 18 July and returns to work on 21 July.

Month 6 (6 September–5 October)
Alan Collins is off sick from 17 August and returns on 31 August.

Month 7 (6 October–5 November)
No variations.

Month 8 (6 November–5 December)
No variations. On 7 November, Helen Doyle shows you a letter from her doctor confirming that she is expecting her baby on 26 April. She could leave on 4 February, but chooses to leave on 9 February. She has worked for the company for three years, full time. Notify her of her maternity pay entitlements.

Month 9 (6 December–5 January)
Lee Sui Yen was off sick from 11 December. She was fit for work on 16 December.

Month 10 (6 January–5 February)
Abe Smith gives his notice in. He will be leaving on 28 February.

Month 11 (6 February–5 March)
Helen Doyle's maternity leave starts on 11 February. Prepare forms SMP2 and SMP3. She will get higher rate SMP for the six weeks from 11 February–24 March and £39.25 per week after that for eleven weeks.
    Leave Mr A.B. Smith's pay until Task 7.

Data for Tasks 1–6 showing separate monthly information – variations from normal pay

TASK 1

This task is to be completed on one day with Tasks 2, 3 and 4.
    For this task you will need (from the *Tutor's Resource Pack*) a page from the wages book, a blank cheque, a pay advice slip, some P11 forms, a pay slip booklet, a Girobank slip and a credit transfer form.
    Check the list of monthly information above for any special facts you will need to know for the next payroll month.
    Complete the wages book page and the P11 forms for the month, using the correct tax and NI tables.

TASK 2

Record the month's figures in the pay slip booklet P30BC(Z) and fill out the Girobank slip P30B(Z) and a cheque for the correct amount, ready for signing by the accountant.

TASK 3

Photocopy the pay advice slips and cheques for the employees, fill the slips in and write out a cheque for each, ready for signing by the accountant. Ask your tutor to sign all the cheques, then prepare wages envelopes for all staff.

TASK 4

Issue the pay packets to colleagues and ask them to sign in the wages book as proof that they have received their 'pay'.

TASK 5

Repeat Task 3, but assume that employees are to be paid by credit transfer.

TASK 6

You need to repeat Tasks 1 to 3 for three more months. Check the list of monthly information (page 116) for the special details for these months.

Record the dates on which you carried out these payroll runs under these two headings: 'Month of payroll' and 'Date done'.

TASK 7

Your supervisor will give you a completed P11 for Mr Smith up to month 10. Mr Smith will be leaving on 28 February and is due for seven days' holiday pay. Complete his wages calculation, then total his P11 form for him and complete a P45.

TASK 8

Tax codes are a source of much confusion for employees. Find out how tax codes are calculated. If your supervisor has a copy of leaflet P3(T), you will find this very useful. If not, you might write off to your local tax office for one.

Type a standard memo to give to employees who ask about tax codes, giving a simple explanation of how they work, and what action to take if they think that their tax code is wrong.

TASK 9

Companies sometimes deduct amounts from employees for reasons other than tax or NI. For example, they may lend employees enough to buy a yearly train season ticket, and then deduct the loan in twelve equal instalments. Of course, the company often has to borrow the money from the bank and to pay interest on it.

Find out the likely rate of interest on Soft Soap's overdraft and put together a proposal for Mr Raj for employee loans for travel purposes. Your proposal should include a table of payments – for example:

Amount of loan	Loan period	Monthly repayment	Weekly repayment

Explain in a memo to Mr Raj how, if an employee takes such a loan, it is recovered through his/her weekly or monthly pay.

TASK 10

Mr Raj feels that it would be a good incentive to employees if the company were to operate a private pension scheme. He has heard terms like 'contracted in' and 'contracted out' but isn't at all sure what they mean. He asks you to explain things to him in non-specialist terms, and also what benefits both employer and employee would get from such a scheme.

Make brief notes on the subject ready to show to your tutor. Your notes should give some detail on:

(a) the state basic and additional pension schemes

(b) adding private schemes which are (i) contracted in and (ii) contracted out

(c) the benefits to the company

(d) the benefits to the employees

TASK 11

Mr Raj has decided to visit France for a couple of months to investigate setting up a production unit and small sales force. He will need funds regularly to keep him going.

Find out how to make an international money transfer from Soft Soap's account to a new account in Paris which Mr Raj has arranged to open.

MAINTAINING FINANCIAL RECORDS

Maintain cash book, day book and ledger records

INTRODUCTION

What do you have to do?

▷ maintain cash books, sales and purchases books and ledgers, and use them to prepare VAT returns and statements of accounts, including aged debts

How well do you have to do it?

To achieve this you must be able to:

▷ enter transactions into account books and computerised accounts systems

▷ total and balance books correctly

▷ prepare VAT returns

▷ prepare statements, including aged debt statements

What do you need to know?

▷ how double-entry book-keeping is done

▷ the role of an accounts department within an organisation

▷ the use of different types of account book

▷ the requirements for preparing VAT returns

What do you need to be able to do?

Using both manual and computerised systems you must be able to:

▷ record income and expenditure in cash books

▷ total cash book columns correctly

▷ record purchase and sales invoices in day books

▷ post cash book and day book transactions into ledgers

▷ prepare statements, including aged debt statements, from ledgers

▷ prepare VAT returns

▷ identify the difference between manual and computerised accounts systems

BACKGROUND KNOWLEDGE

Companies need to keep accurate financial records for many reasons. They have to pay their debts to their suppliers, and obtain payments from their customers. They need to prepare VAT returns and annual accounts. Different types of account book are used to do this.

Cash books record money received by the organisation (**income**), and money sent out (**expenditure**, such as bills paid). In some systems, both income and expenditure are recorded in one cash book; in others, there is a separate book for each. The money may be received in cash or more commonly as cheques. Cash books also record **standing orders** or **direct debits** on the company's bank account. These are used for paying regular bills like rent or water rates. Cash books have to be totalled up at the end of a period (usually monthly).

Day books record invoices that the company receives from its suppliers, and invoices that it issues for goods supplied to its customers. These invoices are recorded as they arrive in the post, or are sent out, so will not normally have been paid when they are entered.

Entries that are made in sales day books and the income cash book are **credits** to the organisation (money coming in). These entries are also duplicated in the **sales ledger**, which shows the amount as a **debit** to the customer (money the customer owes the organisation). Every credit entry has a corresponding debit entry – hence the name **double-entry book-keeping**.

There are often corresponding ledgers for the purchase side. These ledgers contain one page for each major customer or supplier, showing the current state of each individual account. These pages can be used to prepare a **statement** showing how much is owed to a supplier, or how much each of your customers owes you.

In particular, some bills may not have been settled by the due date. These become **aged debts** and need to be chased up for payment, to make sure that an even **cash flow** is maintained by the company.

Every three months, the account books are used to prepare a **Value Added Tax return**. You pay VAT on most of the supplies and services that your company uses, although some categories are **zero rated** or **exempt**. You also charge VAT to your customers on the value of goods or services that you supply to them. These two amounts have to be totalled up and balanced against each other.

If your organisation is doing well, you will be collecting more VAT from your customers than you have paid out, and you will owe the VAT office the difference between the two sums. New companies are often paying out more VAT than they are collecting, as their turnover is low to start with. In this case, the VAT office will pay them back the difference between the two sums.

Because there is a great deal of routine work involved in keeping account books, and many tedious if straightforward calculations to be done, many organisations prefer to use a **computerised accounting system**. There are several accounts packages to choose from, which can automate the process of keeping books and preparing statements, VAT returns and annual accounts. These packages require any transaction to be entered only once. The computer takes care of the double-entry, as well as all the calculations, and prints statements or returns when they are needed.

THE TASKS

Background to the tasks – Soft Soap Ltd

You may be able to practise the skills of book-keeping on real account books or a computerised accounts system within your own workplace/training centre.

The tasks that follow refer to Soft Soap Ltd, the example company used in Unit 3, Element 3.3 *Update records in a computerised database*, and Unit 13 *Information processing*. Soft Soap keeps a simple set of books. There are virtually no cash transactions, so the two cash books show cheques issued and standing orders paid (expenditure) and cheques received (income).

Their sales day book is used to record all invoices issued by the accounts department, and these invoices are then posted to the correct page of the sales ledger. There is one page for each customer so that statements of outstanding accounts can be quickly prepared.

The purchases day book shows only incoming invoices and allows Soft Soap to see how much they owe at any one time. They are too small to need a separate purchases ledger at the moment.

The number of customers and suppliers has been kept small so that the tasks do not become too complex or long-winded, but in a real company the number of entries in account books would be much larger.

Resources required by students/trainees

You will each require photocopies of the following:

▷ Task 1 – the four invoices – one copy; the purchases day book page – one copy

▷ Task 2 – the three invoices – one copy; the sales day book page – one copy; the five ledger pages – one copy

▷ Tasks 3 and 4 – the four outgoing cheques – one copy; the six incoming cheques – one copy; the cash book income page – one copy; the cash book expenditure page – one copy

▷ Task 5 – the blank statement form – you may photocopy as many as you require

DIARY FOR THE YEAR   *for reference purposes*

APRIL

M	T	W	T	F	S	S
1	2	3	4	5	6	7
8	9	10	11	12	13	14
15	16	17	18	19	20	21
22	23	24	25	26	27	28
29	30					

MAY

M	T	W	T	F	S	S
		1	2	3	4	5
6	7	8	9	10	11	12
13	14	15	16	17	18	19
20	21	22	23	24	25	26
27	28	29	30	31		

JUNE

M	T	W	T	F	S	S
					1	2
3	4	5	6	7	8	9
10	11	12	13	14	15	16
17	18	19	20	21	22	23
24	25	26	27	28	29	30

JULY

M	T	W	T	F	S	S
1	2	3	4	5	6	7
8	9	10	11	12	13	14
15	16	17	18	19	20	21
22	23	24	25	26	27	28
29	30	31				

AUGUST

M	T	W	T	F	S	S
			1	2	3	4
5	6	7	8	9	10	11
12	13	14	15	16	17	18
19	20	21	22	23	24	25
26	27	28	29	30	31	

SEPTEMBER

M	T	W	T	F	S	S
						1
2	3	4	5	6	7	8
9	10	11	12	13	14	15
16	17	18	19	20	21	22
23	24	25	26	27	28	29
30						

OCTOBER

M	T	W	T	F	S	S
	1	2	3	4	5	6
7	8	9	10	11	12	13
14	15	16	17	18	19	20
21	22	23	24	25	26	27
28	29	30	31			

NOVEMBER

M	T	W	T	F	S	S
				1	2	3
4	5	6	7	8	9	10
11	12	13	14	15	16	17
18	19	20	21	22	23	24
25	26	27	28	29	30	

DECEMBER

M	T	W	T	F	S	S
						1
2	3	4	5	6	7	8
9	10	11	12	13	14	15
16	17	18	19	20	21	22
23	24	25	26	27	28	29
30	31					

JANUARY

M	T	W	T	F	S	S
	1	2	3	4	5	6
7	8	9	10	11	12	13
14	15	16	17	18	19	20
21	22	23	24	25	26	27
28	29	30	31			

FEBRUARY

M	T	W	T	F	S	S
				1	2	3
4	5	6	7	8	9	10
11	12	13	14	15	16	17
18	19	20	21	22	23	24
25	26	27	28			

MARCH

M	T	W	T	F	S	S
				1	2	3
4	5	6	7	8	9	10
11	12	13	14	15	16	17
18	19	20	21	22	23	24
25	26	27	28	29	30	31

Entering transactions in income and expenditure cash books
Your tutor will give you some accounts pages and transactions to process.

TASK 1 Your tutor will give you four invoices which have been received in the morning's post. Enter them into the page of the purchases day book supplied.

TASK 2 The invoices that your tutor will give you are ready to be sent out to customers for goods recently delivered.

(a) Enter them into the sales day book page provided.

(b) Post these transactions into the sales ledger pages provided.

TASK 3 The transactions for this task consist of four expenditure cheques and six payments received from your customers.

There are also two cash book pages, one for income and one for expenditure.

(a) Enter the transactions in the correct cash book.

(b) Record the cash transactions against the correct invoices in the purchases day book used in Task 1.

(c) Record the cheque payments from customers in the sales ledger pages from Task 2.

TASK 4 The transactions you entered in Task 3 are the last few for the month of February. Total all the columns on both cash books for the month of February.

Check totals against VAT and net amount to make sure that all figures have been correctly recorded.

TASK 5 Using the sales ledger pages from Task 2, prepare a statement for each customer to show any outstanding amounts. Photocopy sufficient of the statements forms supplied by your tutor to complete all the statements.

In a similar way, you could prepare statements of aged debts (those overdue by more than a month, say).

TASK 6 List all payments that are owed to your own suppliers from the purchases day book page from Task 1.

Design a simple form with headed columns to record them on.

Calculate a figure for total owings and show it on your form.